HOW TO CALCULATE QUICKLY

(the art of calculation)

BY HENRY STICKER

DOVER PUBLICATIONS, INC.

Library of Congress Catalog Card Number: 56-3700

Manufactured in the United States of America

Dover Publications, Inc.
180 Varick Street
New York 14, N. Y.

PREFACE

Arithmetic is a science, but calculation is an art. Science is knowledge—art is skill. You have all the knowledge you could possibly need to determine that 57 times 25 equals 1425, but if you are asked to multiply 57 by 25 and cannot do this mentally in just about one second, you are not adept at the art of calculation.

Genuine skill in the calculating art can be acquired by any person of ordinary intelligence, no matter what his schooling may have been. To develop such skill is the purpose of this book. Special forms of short, graded exercises, performed for the most part mentally, lead the student by easy steps to a point where he will possess really exceptional calculating ability.

For instance, if you will look at Exercise No. 371 on page 191, you will find that you are expected to perform mentally such multiplications as 696 times 858, 858 times 878, etc. These are not "trick" examples—the student who systematically performs the practice examples presented in this book will be able to do many kinds of examples of this degree of difficulty by his sheer ability to hold and manipulate figures *in his head*.

How is this skill developed? Essentially by developing *number sense*. Number sense consists in the ability to recognize the relations that exist between numbers considered as whole quantities, and to work with the thought of their broad relations always uppermost. Number sense is possessed by many people in all walks of life—particularly by accountants, bookkeepers, estimators, cashiers, storekeepers and the like. On the other hand, it is absent in many who have an excellent understanding of advanced mathe-

matics. The engineering professions are full of
those who require slide rules to perform calculations which the average billing clerk would do
mentally.

To give an example of what is meant by number sense, suppose you were asked to multiply
mentally 11625 by 12. If you felt at all compe-
tent to try to do so, you would probably (unless
you are the exceptional case) proceed like this:
12 times 5 is 60, remember 0 and carry 6; 12
times 2 is 24, put 0 before the other 0 and carry
3, etc. In this way you would eventually arrive
at the correct answer—if you did not get all
mixed up in the meantime; but at best you would
take a long time, because number sense would
have played no part whatever in your awkward
method of approaching this very simple little
problem.

Suppose now that we introduce a little of this
number sense—suppose that instead of dealing
with plain figures, you were told to imagine that
you had sold twelve machines on each of which
you made a commission of 11.62\frac{1}{2}$. As soon as
money enters into the matter you immediately
see the whole picture in a different light. If you
were asked *approximately* how much your com-
missions amounted to, you would figure quick as
a flash that 11 times 12 is 132, and you would
probably answer instantly that you had made
something over $132. If you were then asked
how much over $132, you would either figure that
62$\frac{1}{2}$¢ are $\frac{5}{8}$ of one dollar, or else that this amount
is equal to half a dollar plus $\frac{1}{8}$ of a dollar. You
would not take long in determining that the ex-
cess over $132 comes to 7\frac{1}{2}$, and that therefore the

total amount received would be $139½ or $139.50.

Why not apply to numbers "in the raw" the same methods that you use when dealing with small amounts of dollars and cents? It is no more difficult to multiply 11⅝ thousands by 12 than 11⅝ dollars. If 11⅝ dollars times 12 is 139½ dollars, then 11⅝ thousands times 12 is 139½ thousands, or 139,500.

From this illustration you may correctly infer that the person with number sense works very largely *from left to right* instead of from right to left. Left-to-right calculation is of the essence of number sense. Countless practical people know this, yet the art of left-to-right calculation is never taught in the schools, and is, in fact, rarely mentioned in books of any kind.

Step-by-step instruction and practice in this neglected art of left-to-right calculation constitutes the greater part of the substance of this book. Methods of this kind are applied not only to multiplication but to all the fundamental operations. By means of such methods, for instance, you learn to add two columns of figures at a time, and you even get a little practice in three-column addition. You are also taught comparable methods of subtraction and division.

In addition to the exercises having to do with left-to-right calculation, there are many that are based on an *extension of the multiplication table.* You are taught by easy stages to use all the numbers up to 25 as direct multipliers—that is to say, you acquire a *complete* knowledge of the multiplication table up to 25 times 25.

The subject of fractions is treated with special reference to the addition and subtraction of the

fractions that are most commonly met with in everyday work. The object here is to enable the student to memorize the answers to the kinds of problems that are ordinarily figured out over and over again.

The exercises dealing with decimals are designed to give the student a large workable fund of knowledge of the decimal equivalents of fractions. Memory work includes twelfths and sixteenths, and there is practice in the rapid calculation of thirty-seconds and twenty-fourths.

The final broad subject developed in this book is "short cuts." These are of the highest value in developing a general understanding of numbers.

The subject matter of this book is limited to the four fundamental operations, with the inclusion of fractions and decimals. No attempt is made to consider the various fields of arithmetical application. Skill in calculation pure and simple is the only goal.

The exercises, nearly four hundred in number, are for the most part very short. Few should take more than ten minutes to do, and many will take less. As progress is by graded steps, the instruction is in small "doses." The book, accordingly, can be used with profit whenever you happen to have a few free minutes. Its pocket size, moreover, makes it all the more suitable for odd-moment study.

Taken as a whole, this book will prove valuable to anybody engaged in work or study that requires any considerable amount of arithmetical calculation. It is especially recommended to heads of departments in industrial and commercial organizations, for general distribution to the members of their staffs.

CONTENTS

1

THE PLAN OF THIS BOOK

The subject matter here presented might have been divided into sections on addition, subtraction, multiplication, etc., in the manner usual to text-books on arithmetic. Because, however, of the special purpose of this book, no such division is made. The general plan is to have several branches proceed simultaneously. Progress is not from subject to subject but from less to more difficult calculation.

For each of the fundamental divisions of arithmetic there is a general introduction—for instance, *Addition in General* on page 3 . In these introductions the special objects sought are described, as well as the methods by which these objects are attained. The student, therefore, always has a clear view of the ultimate aims of his studies and knows how the work immediately in hand fits into the general plan.

Wherever anything new is introduced, it is clearly explained and illustrated. Usually the exercises that go with each explanation are spread through many succeeding pages. In a large number of cases the exercise calls for work with the numbers in a certain list or table (for instance, Table I on page 7). The same lists of numbers are used for various kinds of calculation. This method of presentation makes possible the remarkably great number (about 15,000) of practice examples that are included.

ADDITION IN GENERAL

Two main objects are sought. The first is to add by single columns, grouping three successive numbers at a time; the second is to add two columns at a time:

Take the following sum:

$$
\begin{array}{r}
26 \\
43 \\
84 \\
72 \\
96 \\
27 \\
42 \\
35 \\
68 \\
64 \\
37 \\
\underline{97}
\end{array}
$$

By the first method, starting at the top of the units' column, we would add these numbers thus: (sum of the first three figures) 13 (+ sum of the next three figures, 15) 28 (+ 15) 43 (+ 18) 61; write 1 and carry 6; (6 + 14) 20 (+ 18) 38 (+ 13) 51 (+ 18) 69; total, 691.

By the second method, starting at the top, we would add both columns simultaneously thus: (26 + 43) 69 (+ 84) 153 (+ 72) 225 (+ 96) 321 (+ 27) 348 (+ 42) 390 (+ 35) 425 (+ 68) 493 (+ 64) 557 (+ 37) 594 (+ 97) 691.

In actual practice, very rapid addition is possible by either method, and you will be left free

to choose whichever you prefer. You should, however, learn both.

How do you proceed to learn these methods? You were taught—or should have been taught—at school that speed in addition is acquired by combining pairs of successive numbers that add up to 10. It is at this point that we start, because this is the simplest way in which grouped numbers can be added to a preceding sum. You are given short columns of numbers to be added by incidentally selecting such pairs of successive figures as make 10. In succeeding exercises the columns are lengthened, and you are also asked to group any pairs that add up to less than 10.

In the meantime, you will have been doing exercises in mentally adding all the numbers from 11 to 18 to all the numbers from 1 to 99. Since no pair of figures in a column can add to more than 18, this amount of practice will enable you to add *any* pair of successive figures in a column to a previous sum, and hence to add the entire column by taking two figures at a time.

You are similarly taught to add trios of numbers that make 10 or less than 10, and to add any number from 19 to 27 to any number from 1 to 99. With this practice you will be able to add *any* column by taking three figures at a time.

If you can quickly add any number from 1 to 27 to another number, you will not find it difficult to add numbers greater than 27 in the same manner. You are accordingly ready now to add two columns at a time. Exercises in this method are introduced, and these are gradually increased in difficulty.

Toward the end of the book there are some exercises in three-column addition—just enough to demonstrate that it will be possible for *you* to add this way if you wish to use this method.

There are examples in addition of still another kind. These are not included for practice in addition as such but have a special bearing on the art of multiplying mentally. We need not consider sums of this kind at this point.

You will note that in the exercises in one-column addition you are alternately instructed *to add from the top down* and *to add from the bottom up.* In practical work it is of course immaterial in which direction addition is performed. You should, however, be able to add with equal facility in either direction, and by alternating as suggested you will get the necessary practice.

Exercise No. 1

Pairs Adding to 10

Add the following columns by grouping pairs of numbers that make 10. *Add from the top down.*

Thus you would add the first column by saying to yourself: 7, 17, 22, 32.

Do not consciously repeat in your mind anything but the successive totals. That is to say, do *not* add this column thus: 7 + 10, 17, +5, 22, +10, 32.

For another illustration of the correct method, take the second example. This is added thus: 8, 18, 20, 30.

Write your answers in succession on a piece of paper and compare them with the correct answers on page 154. (A good plan is to place the edge of your paper immediately under the examples, write the answers along this edge, and fold it under as it becomes used up.)

1. 7	2. 8	3. 4	4. 5	5. 6	6. 5
6	9	5	2	4	5
4	1	5	8	6	3
5	2	5	4	3	6
1	3	4	1	2	4
9	7	6	9	8	8

7. 5	8. 3	9. 8	10. 6	11. 5	12. 9
4	2	2	9	5	6
6	7	9	1	3	4
6	3	8	5	2	8
3	1	1	4	4	1
7	2	9	6	6	7

13. 3	14. 1	15. 6	16. 6	17. 1	18. 7
7	9	4	3	3	6
6	9	4	7	7	2
2	1	5	2	9	8
8	5	4	2	3	5
8	4	3	5	7	5

19. 1	20. 1	21. 6	22. 3	23. 7	24. 4
9	5	4	4	5	9
4	5	7	6	5	1
3	9	6	4	3	3
9	4	3	6	6	2
1	6	7	3	2	8

Table I
Numbers from 1 to 99

1	8	15	22	29	36	43	50
57	64	71	78	85	92	99	6
13	20	27	34	41	48	55	62
69	76	83	90	97	4	11	18
25	32	39	46	53	60	67	74
81	88	95	2	9	16	23	30
37	44	51	58	65	72	79	86
93	7	14	21	28	35	42	49
56	63	70	77	84	91	98	5
12	19	26	33	40	47	54	61
68	75	82	89	96	3	10	17
24	31	38	45	52	59	66	73
80	87	94					

Exercise No. 2
Mental Addition

Add 11 to each of the numbers in Table I above.

Use *left-to-right* addition, which is performed by first adding the tens of one number to the whole of another. In other words, starting with the number in the table you first add 10 and then 1. A few illustrations will be in order:

15 + 11: say 15, 25, 26;

22 + 11: say 22, 32, 33;

29 + 11: say 29, 39, 40;

99 + 11: say 99, 109, 110.

Work down the columns—not across the page. Write down your answers and compare them with those on page 154.

Exercise No. 3
Pairs Adding to 10

Group all pairs of successive numbers that make 10.
Add from the bottom up.

1. 7	2. 6	3. 5	4. 9	5. 6	6. 3
8	4	2	7	7	1
4	5	5	6	9	6
6	2	4	4	1	4
5	4	6	8	3	4
3	5	6	8	4	1
5	4	7	9	6	8
5	1	3	1	3	2
1	2	4	1	8	9
8	8	8	7	5	6
2	7	2	5	2	4
5	3	4	5	8	7

7. 4	8. 8	9. 4	10. 6	11. 9	12. 3
7	2	4	5	8	7
3	9	3	7	8	6
8	1	2	3	2	6
3	5	4	4	7	1
2	3	6	2	1	2
2	8	1	8	9	7
8	5	6	9	6	6
1	5	4	1	5	4
9	2	9	3	5	5
1	6	3	2	5	5
9	5	7	1	4	6

13. 7	14. 3	15. 9	16. 1	17. 3	18. 6
4	7	1	8	6	9
6	8	6	7	4	1
3	2	3	5	2	7
2	8	7	5	8	7
6	5	5	6	5	3
4	5	4	7	1	2
1	8	6	3	4	1
8	2	4	5	1	5
3	7	3	4	9	2
7	1	2	4	3	9
9	9	9	6	7	1

Exercise No. 4
Mental Addition

Add 12 to the numbers in Table I on page 7.

To illustrate:

15 + 12: say 15, 25, 27;

22 + 12: say 22, 32, 34;

29 + 12: say 29, 39, 41;

99 + 12: say 99, 109, 111.

Exercise No. 5
Mental Addition

Add 13 to the numbers in Table I on page 7.

Exercise No. 6
Mental Addition

Add 14 to the numbers in Table I on page 7.

Exercise No. 7

Mental Addition

Add 15 to the numbers in Table I on page 7.

Exercise No. 8

Pairs Adding to 10 or Less

The grouping of pairs of successive numbers is now to be extended to include any that add to less than 10 as well as any that add to 10. That is to say, as you add each column watch to see whether any two successive numbers add to either 10 or less than 10, and if they do, make one addition of them to the preceding sum.

For this exercise use the columns of numbers in Exercise No. 1 and compare your answers with those for Exercise No. 1. *Add from the top down.*

To illustrate, the first column is added: 7, 17, 23, 32; the second: 8, 18, 23, 30; the third: 9, 19, 29.

Exercise No. 9

Mental Addition

Add 16 to each of the numbers in Table I on page 7.

Exercise No. 10

Mental Addition

Add 17 to each of the numbers in Table I on page 7.

Exercise No. 11

Pairs Adding to 10 or Less

Add the columns in Exercise No. 3 by grouping all pairs of successive numbers that add to 10 or less than 10. *Add from the bottom up.*

Exercise No. 12

Mental Addition

Add 18 to each of the numbers in Table I on page 7.

Exercise No. 13

Adding Single Columns by Pairs

Add the following by single columns, taking pairs of successive numbers at a time. *Add from the top down.* The first example would be added: 5, 14, 25, write 5 and carry 2; 2, 12, 27, 36; answer 365.

1. 43	2. 29	3. 58	4. 87	5. 16
62	75	33	62	91
78	36	65	94	33
81	69	98	27	56
14	43	72	89	29
87	16	45	74	32

6. 19	7. 48	8. 77	9. 36	10. 63
99	21	29	49	78
36	68	49	94	96
71	29	11	59	44
61	18	51	22	41
41	25	53	27	88

11. 33	12. 21	13. 34	14. 24	15. 16
39	79	43	14	44
43	74	27	11	49
51	85	53	15	54
55	63	17	75	49
36	82	57	78	99

16. 31	17. 28	18. 63	19. 32	20. 63
35	63	35	65	28
67	21	12	16	76
44	34	31	67	45
84	52	81	73	69
42	56	15	55	62

21. 85	22. 54	23. 14	24. 68	25. 69
56	42	27	42	28
75	68	54	28	45
37	13	85	34	37
73	99	59	83	71
24	84	69	16	91

Exercise No. 14
Mental Addition

Add 19 to each of the numbers in Table I on page 7 .

Exercise No. 15
Adding Single Columns by Pairs

Add the following by single columns, taking pairs of successive numbers at a time. *Add from the bottom up.* The first example would be added: 11, 15, 27, 42, 49, 60, write 0 and carry 6; 6, 17, 24, 37, 43, 54, 62; answer, 620.

1. 27	2. 81	3. 92	4. 16	5. 29
64	28	92	14	27
32	75	29	14	25
85	43	86	31	25
46	96	54	97	32
29	57	18	65	19
78	51	68	29	76
64	89	62	79	51
31	75	11	73	12
43	42	86	22	84
75	54	53	58	33
46	86	65	64	19

6. 43	7. 58	8. 74	9. 91	10. 99
51	54	69	85	13
38	62	65	91	96
36	49	74	76	13
37	47	71	85	87
33	36	58	82	96
41	34	47	69	93
87	52	35	58	87
62	98	63	37	69
23	73	31	74	47
95	34	84	42	75
44	27	45	95	53

11. 19	12. 39	13. 51	14. 63	15. 84
12	41	55	62	99
26	23	52	62	75
18	37	34	63	73
24	29	48	45	74
24	35	56	59	56
18	98	46	67	82
15	29	31	57	78
98	26	53	42	68
36	91	37	64	53
85	48	13	48	59
49	96	59	24	57

Exercise No. 16
Mental Addition
Add 20 to each of the numbers in Table I on page 7.

Exercise No. 17
Adding Single Columns by Pairs
Add the following by single columns, taking pairs of successive numbers at a time. *Add from the top down.*

1. 51	2. 42	3. 41	4. 34	5. 33
30	53	73	36	81
96	90	32	97	28
24	79	12	19	39
25	87	62	69	43
75	76	11	94	10
48	92	44	83	85
49	52	84	37	47
93	45	70	38	29
80	72	40	46	14
13	18	61	17	95
58	63	67	23	10
88	22	56	66	82
86	21	16	64	31
20	59	98	89	77
99	91	55	68	74
59	15	27	60	35
65	78	54	23	84

6. 61	7. 34	8. 39	9. 36	10. 17
81	90	32	25	66
82	86	21	97	28
24	85	49	96	74
59	16	87	52	84
95	58	33	30	15
53	64	48	63	67
37	47	11	94	93
27	23	60	35	73
31	45	20	62	69
92	44	70	51	10
83	65	26	91	29
80	72	55	88	79
38	68	57	43	78
54	42	12	19	22
98	40	46	14	13
41	89	75	56	76
77	99	18	42	39

Exercise No. 18

Mental Addition

Add 21 to each of the numbers in Table I on page 7 .

SUBTRACTION IN GENERAL

In keeping with the general object of this book, the succeeding exercises in subtraction are performed by left-to-right methods.

When subtraction is performed on paper there is no special advantage in working from left to right instead of from right to left. Paper practice in the former method, however, fits in with the broad purpose of developing number sense.

When it comes to doing subtraction mentally, the left-to-right method is natural and logical. Thus, if you had started the day with $17.43 in your pocket, and if you wanted to figure without paper and pencil how much you had left after spending $5.89, you would not be likely to start by subtracting 9 from 13. You would probably calculate that if you had spent the full $6, you would have $11.43 left, but that having spent 11¢ less than $6, the remainder comes to 11¢ more than $11.43, or $11.54.

In considering the specific aims of these exercises in subtraction, look first at the written examples. If you will glance at the first exercise that follows, and which is included merely to familiarize you with the idea of working from left to right, you will see that in every case the figures in the subtrahend (lower number) are smaller than those in the minuend. The examples are all of the type of

$$\begin{array}{r} 54 \\ -23 \\ \hline \end{array}$$

17

and you can determine the answers faster than you can write them down. If, however, you take the example

$$685$$
$$-356$$

and try to write the answer in the same way, you will run into trouble when you reach the final figures at the right because 6 is greater than 5. What to do about cases of this kind is the subject of the instruction. The exercises take into account the possible variations that may occur in numbers of two and three places.

The examples in mental subtraction are performed by methods altogether different from those that apply to written work. There are two such methods, of which one has already been illustrated. We subtracted $5.89 from $17.43 by taking $6 from $17.43 and then adding to $11.43 the difference between $6 and $5.89, obtaining as our answer $11.43 + $.11, or $11.54. To do the same example mentally by the other method, we calculate that if you had started with $17 even, you would have $11.11 left; but you had $.43 more than $17 at the start, and therefore the actual remainder is $11.11 + $.43, or $11.54. One method is as good as the other. Examples are given that carry the practice in both methods as far as numbers involving hundreds of dollars and odd cents.

Incidentally, you should know that ordinary written subtraction is commonly performed by two entirely different methods—the *borrow*

method and the *carry* method. The borrow method is taught almost exclusively in this country today, but in times past the carry method had similar acceptance.

Take the example

$$
\begin{array}{r}
856 \\
-569 \\
\hline
287
\end{array}
$$

To do this by the borrow method you reason: 9 from 16 leaves 7, 6 from 14 leaves 8, 5 from 7 leaves 2; answer, 287. To do the same example by the carry method you would say: 9 from 16 leaves 7, 7 from 15 leaves 8, 6 from 8 leaves 2; answer, 287.

You should understand both these methods (neither of which has any clear advantage over the other), though you continue to use regularly whichever one comes most naturally to you. In the illustrations given in this book the borrow method is followed because it is the more familiar to the majority of people.

Exercise No. 19
Left-to-Right Subtraction

Perform the following subtractions by directly writing your answers from left to right.

1. 67	2. 48	3. 41	4. 78	5. 64
55	14	20	22	31

6. 98	7. 53	8. 65	9. 28	10. 66
20	41	52	16	45

11. 99　**12.** 69　**13.** 83　**14.** 32　**15.** 93
　　92　　　35　　　31　　　21　　　41

Exercise No. 20

Left-to-Right Subtraction

Directly write your answers from left to right.

To take the first example, you simply note that 6 is greater than 4, and therefore the 5 in the minuend becomes a 4: 2 from 4 leaves 2 (writing 2), 6 from 14 leaves 8 (writing 8); answer 28.

1. 54　**2.** 47　**3.** 51　**4.** 46　**5.** 52
　　26　　　19　　　39　　　27　　　37

6. 84　**7.** 37　**8.** 35　**9.** 72　**10.** 50
　　58　　　18　　　17　　　24　　　29

11. 83　**12.** 56　**13.** 71　**14.** 96　**15.** 77
　　44　　　39　　　45　　　38　　　49

16. 94　**17.** 45　**18.** 48　**19.** 68　**20.** 71
　　76　　　16　　　29　　　39　　　52

Exercise No. 21

Mental Addition

Add 22 to each of the numbers in Table I on page 7.

Exercise No. 22

Trios that Add to 10 or Less

This exercise introduces the idea of taking in three suc-

cessive numbers at a glance. Every column contains four
groups of three numbers each; each of these groups adds
to 10 or less. Add by combining these groups. *Add from
the top down.*

1. 27	2. 14	3. 64	4. 57	5. 34
21	11	21	31	31
11	12	13	12	11
45	33	44	56	54
41	21	42	21	42
13	13	22	23	13
65	25	43	56	52
12	21	32	12	31
12	24	33	12	22
25	35	78	45	44
11	12	11	21	31
11	13	11	12	14

6. 41	7. 62	8. 43	9. 21	10. 33
21	32	33	11	12
26	12	24	15	15
31	61	21	12	63
31	21	11	11	11
22	23	27	14	24
81	52	43	33	42
11	21	11	11	22
11	16	45	23	44
72	44	62	24	43
21	12	12	21	32
13	14	15	25	33

Exercise No. 23

Left-to-Right Subtraction

Sight practice with pairs of three-place numbers. No borrowings are involved. Work from left to right.

1. 754	2. 827	3. 468	4. 659	5. 746
233	614	235	338	415

6. 928	7. 675	8. 558	9. 649	10. 458
615	423	146	437	328

11. 727	12. 898	13. 753	14. 462	15. 941
605	457	321	111	720

Exercise No. 24

Mental Addition

Add 23 to each of the numbers in Table I on page 7.

Exercise No. 25

Mental Addition

Add 24 to each of the numbers in Table I on page 7.

Exercise No. 26

Adding Single Columns by Pairs

Take successive pairs at a time. *Add from the top down.*

1. $40.72	**2.** $35.51	**3.** $27.13	**4.** $47.15
33.32	56.28	96.92	10.20
98.21	43.90	22.07	36.09
29.05	49.44	38.71	59.73
53.69	84.57	58.94	55.70
79.66	99.61	34.88	85.54
83.97	24.25	60.26	31.78
45.77	16.23	65.14	11.12
42.63	80.17	18.19	52.48
46.68	82.67	89.30	87.81
64.39	86.93	41.75	74.01
37.62	91.76	50.95	25.60

5. $79.45	**6.** $77.52	**7.** $48.68	**8.** $88.09
85.30	54.05	49.99	44.80
70.46	61.65	14.78	75.03
83.73	76.29	11.12	36.53
69.97	74.43	90.55	95.96
34.21	38.10	17.18	62.39
64.81	87.37	15.50	82.01
20.72	63.25	56.47	26.13
60.26	32.93	67.06	33.28
31.57	22.98	19.16	42.71
59.86	89.84	41.40	94.66
58.35	91.23	56.15	10.34

Exercise No. 27

Left-to-Right Subtraction

In these examples, in the vertical pairs of figures at the extreme right the subtrahend is greater than the minuend, reducing by 1 the tens' figure of the minuend.

Taking the first example, we note that the tens' figure of the minuend will become a 4 instead of a 5; 5 from 7 leaves 2, 3 from 4 leaves 1, 9 from 14 leaves 5; answer 215.

1. 754	2. 863	3. 528	4. 642	5. 995
539	448	319	313	217

6. 422	7. 323	8. 676	9. 266	10. 583
313	109	428	138	346

11. 912	12. 365	13. 744	14. 390	15. 555
509	259	619	265	419

16. 983	17. 696	18. 472	19. 713	20. 626
779	587	329	606	318

21. 718	22. 683	23. 951	24. 648	25. 873
409	246	229	539	358

26. 715	27. 582	28. 246	29. 997	30. 737
506	246	139	129	318

Exercise No. 28

Mental Addition

Add 25 to each of the numbers in Table I on page 7.

Exercise No. 29

Mental Addition

Add 26 to each of the numbers in Table I on page 7.

Exercise No. 30

Mental Addition

Add 27 to each of the numbers in Table I on page 7.

Exercise No. 31

Trios that Add to 20 or Less

In the separate columns of the following examples the successive groups of three figures add to some number between 11 and 20. Add by combining these groups of three. *Add from the top down.*

The first example would be added: 16, 30, 41, 61, write 1 and carry 6; 6, 18, 30, 46, 62; answer 621.

1. 23	2. 31	3. 12	4. 24	5. 24
46	46	84	64	74
67	46	89	74	78
21	12	33	35	35
55	24	43	45	55
58	97	78	95	78
22	13	13	14	14
54	73	37	45	44
95	86	99	75	99
12	23	13	25	25
69	57	88	65	35
99	77	98	86	69

6. 33	7. 32	8. 24	9. 34	10. 24
36	44	67	54	75
98	58	69	56	85
11	13	36	25	35
25	33	47	25	56
89	77	87	89	86
13	23	13	24	14
77	57	48	64	55
75	88	69	97	56
23	31	14	35	25
56	46	99	55	36
69	68	98	67	77

Exercise No. 32
Left-to-Right Subtraction

In the type of example given here we see by inspection that the subtrahend has a larger figure than the minuend in the tens' place, reducing by 1 the hundreds' figure of the minuend. To take the first example: 5 from 6 leaves 1, 9 from 15 leaves 6, 3 from 4 leaves 1; answer 161.

Subtract from left to right.

1. 754	2. 648	3. 262	4. 548	5. 629
593	356	191	357	458

6. 856	7. 435	8. 468	9. 914	10. 765
792	183	271	291	481

11. 787	**12.** 547	**13.** 341	**14.** 112	**15.** 783
693	160	171	51	190

16. 486	**17.** 888	**18.** 489	**19.** 944	**20.** 842
291	494	194	452	161

Exercise No. 33

Left-to-Right Subtraction

In these examples the tens and the units are larger in the subtrahend than in the minuend, thus reducing by 1 both the hundreds and the tens of the minuend. Taking the first example: 2 from 6 leaves 4, 8 from 14 leaves 6, 9 from 14 leaves 5; answer, 465.

1. 754	**2.** 773	**3.** 413	**4.** 484	**5.** 342
289	194	249	298	189

6. 626	**7.** 787	**8.** 383	**9.** 867	**10.** 672
578	298	197	379	295

11. 918	**12.** 666	**13.** 586	**14.** 232	**15.** 515
589	197	298	176	299

16. 353	**17.** 428	**18.** 856	**19.** 481	**20.** 318
169	179	779	192	149

Exercise No. 34
Adding Single Columns by Pairs

Add the following by single columns, taking pairs of successive numbers at a time. *Add from the bottom up.*

1.	2.	3.	4.
$14.44	$80.54	$74.43	$43.93
38.42	33.20	67.27	32.06
72.09	13.40	18.02	94.34
61.90	55.95	21.60	97.86
63.26	10.17	25.98	30.29
56.78	75.79	96.45	36.47
73.76	77.52	89.84	70.66
62.58	39.51	11.12	35.07
91.28	83.85	64.48	81.68
31.41	87.19	19.92	49.37
71.15	59.57	22.53	69.16
50.82	24.23	65.99	57.84
22.78	94.70	66.75	53.69
33.34	61.90	11.54	96.17
25.12	50.05	74.45	36.03
92.49	82.98	55.62	30.35
58.43	93.63	95.37	39.51
75.64	20.67	72.71	48.15

5. $22.78	6. $94.70	7. $66.75	8. $79.53
69.33	34.61	90.72	71.09
48.14	27.10	80.11	54.96
17.81	68.47	73.29	59.15
44.88	76.13	56.25	50.91
40.18	31.05	74.45	57.42
19.02	26.30	35.58	43.93
63.95	37.86	24.38	32.23
89.16	46.65	39.51	85.64
99.08	20.67	84.36	28.41
87.83	92.49	82.98	55.01
77.52	21.60	92.13	16.46
22.78	56.25	49.12	50.91
40.18	31.82	94.70	98.55
66.75	62.77	52.05	74.79
53.45	69.33	34.57	21.65
60.39	51.85	64.61	90.72
71.09	48.15	27.10	80.06

Exercise No. 35

Left-to-Right Subtraction

This exercise illustrates a principle: if a figure in the subtrahend is the same as the one above it in the minuend, the effect on the minuend will depend on whether or not a borrowing has been necessary with the next figure to the right.

In the first example we see that because 9 is greater than 4, the 5 in the minuend becomes a 4, and since 5 is greater than this the 7 in the minuend becomes a 6. We perform the subtraction thus: 3 from 6 leaves 3, 5 from 14 leaves 9, 9 from 14 leaves 5; answer, 395.

1. 754	2. 655	3. 251	4. 546	5. 592
359	358	159	247	294

6. 862	7. 444	8. 968	9. 773	10. 763
667	146	569	279	266

11. 832	12. 233	13. 983	14. 572	15. 656
536	139	488	278	357

16. 395	17. 856	18. 645	19. 721	20. 941
197	659	248	428	249

21. 527	22. 863	23. 985	24. 267	25. 843
329	569	389	168	448

Exercise No. 36

Trios that Add to 27 or Less

The groups of three here add to numbers between 21 and 27. Add by combining these groups. *Add from the top down.*

1. 36	2. 63	3. 47	4. 65	5. 47
98	79	87	78	97
99	89	98	98	99
69	86	74	87	75
99	89	78	87	78
99	89	79	99	89
56	33	67	54	49
89	99	77	89	89
89	99	97	99	99
73	67	84	77	75
79	97	88	87	78
99	97	99	88	78

6. 55	**7.** 68	**8.** 56	**9.** 68	**10.** 56
88	88	87	88	98
89	88	99	99	98
77	85	78	96	78
78	99	88	98	89
98	99	89	98	99
65	57	96	68	66
89	98	97	89	78
89	99	98	99	89
87	76	78	96	84
98	87	78	97	88
98	98	88	99	89

Exercise No. 37

Left-to-Right Subtraction

In these examples another consideration arises: the tens' figure in the minuend is 0; when 1 is borrowed to make possible the subtraction of the units, the tens in the minuend become 9 and the hundreds are also reduced by 1.

To illustrate with the first example: 3 from 6 leaves 3, 5 from 9 leaves 4, 7 from 14 leaves 7; answer, 347.

Subtract from left to right.

1. 704	**2.** 307	**3.** 806	**4.** 204	**5.** 404
357	118	457	126	297

6. 808	**7.** 706	**8.** 308	**9.** 302	**10.** 203
549	517	189	236	115

11. 800	**12.** 501	**13.** 300	**14.** 805	**15.** 601
585	323	122	796	374

16. 902	17. 500	18. 408	19. 700	20. 207
793	386	159	466	178

21. 807	22. 603	23. 200	24. 600	25. 300
509	319	162	224	171

Exercise No. 38
Adding Single Columns by Pairs
Take pairs of successive numbers at a time. *Add from the bottom up.*

1. $5759.37	2. $7856.21	3. $6525.49
2186.62	2477.50	5214.44
4491.67	5843.84	8788.76
3848.60	3993.36	1115.81
6874.79	4751.85	2740.32
1831.04	9213.53	4569.82
1080.33	3363.26	9528.30
6461.73	9994.90	7271.70
9823.34	9617.89	8983.55

4. $4142.97	5. $6675.01	6. $1916.46
4629.22	3508.07	2009.03
2089.83	5624.21	6538.82
9766.48	6039.10	8788.80
3367.72	7677.25	7531.01
9849.04	6393.03	8635.19
1623.26	6257.59	5096.58
4308.52	3646.51	1185.13
5354.34	9678.28	1714.55
4244.07	7170.27	4015.81
6874.79	3229.30	6422.37
6118.91	4569.73	9947.94

Exercise No. 39

Mental Subtraction

Use the method of making the subtrahend a round number. Subtract $1 from the minuend and add to this the difference between $1 and the given subtrahend.

Taking the first example: $1 from $5.18 leaves $4.18; $.83 from $1 leaves $.17; $4.18 + $.17 = $4.35.

1.	$5.18 − $.83	11.	$3.22 − $.93
2.	$6.42 − $.83	12.	$7.37 − $.61
3.	$1.89 − $.95	13.	$4.56 − $.97
4.	$2.47 − $.99	14.	$6.87 − $.91
5.	$7.48 − $.56	15.	$2.21 − $.65
6.	$8.29 − $.66	16.	$4.86 − $.97
7.	$3.18 − $.87	17.	$3.32 − $.64
8.	$7.27 − $.43	18.	$7.75 − $.83
9.	$4.19 − $.49	19.	$4.12 − $.63
10.	$3.53 − $.77	20.	$6.23 − $.26

Exercise No. 40

Adding Single Columns by Trios

Do the addition examples in Exercise No. 13 on page 11 by grouping three numbers at a time.

Taking the first example there presented, the following illustrates the method of adding: 13 (+12) 25, write 5 and carry 2; 2 (+17) 19, (+17) 36; answer, 365. Do not consciously repeat to yourself the individual amounts that you are adding, but only the successive total. *Add from the top down.*

Exercise No. 41

Adding Single Columns by Pairs

1.	$7489.99	2.	$8356.24	3.	$2165.38
	2897.66		4860.39		1034.96
	7828.17		8084.05		8788.86
	3519.16		2303.32		2922.64
	2237.61		1891.45		4142.44
	7170.27		4015.94		9062.57
	5950.95		5843.08		9849.04
	1209.63		9326.73		4768.79
	8152.92		3646.51		1185.13
	5354.14		5520.33		6772.76
	7725.75		3104.60		1348.37
	6101.98		4953.91		6039.62
	5429.30		6772.76		1780.84
	4414.57		5910.18		9134.96
	7812.07		7170.06		8788.86
	5056.24		9564.22		7755.63
	2593.26		2075.27		4033.03
	4569.35		9236.74		8932.58

4. $8799.55	5. $1319.16	6. $8348.84
4437.14	5781.63	2538.82
9793.08	5266.88	2861.41
4223.59	3926.73	9809.50
3218.94	9156.24	5834.43
9564.65	2227.49	5340.33
6296.78	1207.54	5446.31
4569.35	7729.30	5115.71
7006.68	6772.11	8521.65
7976.92	9036.17	8074.89
3612.97	8909.50	2124.56
8765.77	2930.51	1507.23
5960.54	9964.75	2279.76
5546.31	7188.86	2858.34
4347.04	4147.61	8085.37
9570.06	1457.10	4884.44
6935.05	3218.94	8168.39
6774.27	4913.26	7273.93

Exercise No. 42

Mental Subtraction

Perform the subtractions in Exercise No. 39 by using the method of making a round number of the minuend. That is, reduce the minuend to the next lower number of even dollars. Subtract the subtrahend from this and then add the excess of cents in the minuend.

Taking the first example ($5.18 − $.83): $.83 from $5 leaves $4.17; $4.17 + 18 = $4.35.

Exercise No. 43

Mental Subtraction

Perform the following subtractions mentally. Raise the subtrahend to the next larger number of even dollars.

1. $2.79 — $1.86	**11.** $5.53 — $3.64
2. $3.17 — $1.97	**12.** $2.62 — $1.89
3. $9.50 — $6.69	**13.** $3.05 — $1.82
4. $2.56 — $1.91	**14.** $8.28 — $6.65
5. $4.77 — $2.81	**15.** $8.10 — $6.39
6. $9.78 — $3.94	**16.** $5.15 — $2.67
7. $7.44 — $4.49	**17.** $4.47 — $2.61
8. $4.37 — $2.72	**18.** $7.93 — $5.99
9. $5.22 — $2.98	**19.** $5.40 — $2.95
10. $6.04 — $5.33	**20.** $3.23 — $1.60

Exercise No. 44

Mental Subtraction

Do the examples in Exercise No. 43 by lowering the minuend to the next smaller number of even dollars.

MULTIPLICATION IN GENERAL

Multiplication is the heart's core of the art of calculation. In itself it constitutes an art about which a large volume might be written.

The multiplication exercises in this book have three main objects in view—first, to enable the student to use all numbers up to 25 as direct multipliers in written work; second, to teach him to multiply mentally any number up to 1000 by any other number up to 1000; third, to drill him in various short-cut methods that apply to particular cases.

The use of numbers up to 25 as direct multipliers may be illustrated by this example:

A	B
7648	7648
1923	1923
22944	175904
15296	145312
68832	14707104
7648	
14707104	

In Method A, which is here shown for comparison, the usual procedure is followed. In Method B the calculation is performed thus: $8 \times 23 = 184$, write 4 and carry 18; $4 \times 23 = 92$, $92 + 18 = 110$, write 0 and carry 11; $6 \times 23 = 138$, $138 + 11 = 149$, write 9 and carry 14; $7 \times 23 = 161$, $161 + 14 = 175$. Multiplication by 19 is done in the same way, and the partial products added.

To multiply in the manner described it is of course necessary to acquire a knowledge of the multiplication table up to 25 × 25. Instruction in this direction is given by very easy steps. There are several types of exercises leading to the same end.

Exercises in mental multiplication are similarly graded. You start by multiplying two figures by one, then two by two, then three by one, three by two, and finally three by three.

The subject of short cuts is highly specialized and need not detain us for the present.

Exercise No. 45
Mental Multiplication

Multiply by 2 the numbers in Table I on page 7. Proceed from left to right. A few examples of the method calculating will suffice.

32×2: $30 \times 2 = 60, 2 \times 2 = 4, 60 + 4 = 64$
45×2: $40 \times 2 = 80, 5 \times 2 = 10, 80 + 10 = 90$
49×2: $40 \times 2 = 80, 9 \times 2 = 18, 80 + 18 = 98$
99×2: $90 \times 2 = 180, 9 \times 2 = 18, 180 + 18 = 198$

Exercise No. 46
Mental Multiplication

Multiply mentally by 3 the numbers in Table I on page 7.

Exercise No. 47
Mental Multiplication

Multiply mentally by 4 the numbers in Table I on page 7.

Exercise No. 48

Adding Single Columns by Pairs

Take pairs of successive numbers at a time. *Add from the bottom up.*

1. $227976.55	**2.** $364631.71
491368.39	291241.97
476170.02	620314.57
804501.33	378990.83
920950.63	267278.30
512573.15	586721.69

3. $693505.74	**4.** $430413.93
822427.23	525632.59
186620.98	198886.28
871060.54	651653.40
118577.94	964295.81
996475.17	480444.80

5. $605465.38	**6.** $694235.68
599320.95	483929.91
810064.74	841653.40
112279.76	344518.66
431275.17	624133.37
890890.55	364698.97

Exercise No. 49

Mental Subtraction

Raise the subtrahend to the next larger number of even dollars.

1. $19.03 — $.50	**9.** $61.70 — $.94
2. $26.52 — $.86	**10.** $72.04 — $.85
3. $24.27 — $.32	**11.** $67.30 — $.73
4. $15.58 — $.80	**12.** $60.54 — $.69
5. $42.35 — $.59	**13.** $94.20 — $.48
6. $39.29 — $.91	**14.** $81.64 — $.74
7. $16.53 — $.79	**15.** $76.34 — $.66
8. $43.12 — $.17	**16.** $62.41 — $.89

Exercise No. 50

Mental Multiplication

Multiply mentally by 5 the numbers in Table I on page 7.

Exercise No. 51

Mental Subtraction

Do the examples in Exercise No. 49 by reducing the minuend to the next smaller number of even dollars.

Exercise No. 52

Mental Multiplication

Multiply mentally by 6 the numbers in Table I on page 7.

Exercise No. 53

Mental Multiplication

Multiply mentally by 7 the numbers in Table I on page 7.

Exercise No. 54

Adding Single Columns by Pairs

Take pairs of successive numbers at a time. *Add from the top down.*

1.	2.
$806054.65	$386942.35
681097.85	933492.59
451866.93	209507.09
431248.39	751706.02
298291.24	882750.78
322157.61	305181.62
700177.25	733115.33
714913.58	379499.64
746789.23	663265.52
569055.36	444684.16
534011.98	227976.86
281472.87	377730.32

3.	4.
$243130.39	$559663.93
158010.21	882067.60
519794.95	265254.65
893672.07	332750.44
870485.02	380353.71
834913.40	462925.62
287919.76	583492.78
697537.73	411711.98
225942.35	230882.09
435756.84	911270.45
996168.05	180190.66
164864.14	744732.86

Exercise No. 55
Mental Subtraction

Raise the subtrahend to the next larger number of even dollars.

1. $24.31 — $4.55		**9.** $96.15 — $8.88
2. $26.36 — $7.50		**10.** $87.04 — $2.53
3. $49.13 — $4.62		**11.** $79.19 — $7.58
4. $34.37 — $7.98		**12.** $59.42 — $3.82
5. $43.12 — $1.70		**13.** $99.05 — $1.90
6. $14.06 — $7.86		**14.** $77.24 — $3.55
7. $15.10 — $2.88		**15.** $67.60 — $5.97
8. $26.52 — $6.89		**16.** $72.07 — $3.87

Exercise No. 56
Mental Multiplication

Multiply mentally by 8 the numbers in Table I on page 7.

Exercise No. 57
Adding Single Columns by Trios

Do the examples in Exercise No. 15 on page 12 by taking three successive numbers at a time. *Add from the top down.*

Exercise No. 58
Mental Subtraction

Do the examples in Exercise No. 55 by lowering the minuend to the next smaller number of even dollars.

Exercise No. 59
Addition of Partial Products

The type of exercise here presented has a bearing on mental multiplication. Thus the first example represents, in inverted position, the partial products we get when we multiply 15 by 53.

$$
\begin{array}{r}
15 \\
53 \\
\hline
45 \\
750 \\
\hline
795
\end{array}
$$

When partial products of this kind occur in mental multiplication you are of necessity compelled *to retain them in your mind*. Hence to develop your ability to do this kind of memory work, you are asked to read each example once and then write it three times on paper before you perform the mental addition.

Complete the mental addition before writing the answer. Work from left to right. Thus in doing the first example you would say to yourself: 750, 790, 795. In doing the second you would say: 620, 680, 682.

1. 750	2. 620	3. 470	4. 740	5. 520
45	62	94	74	78
6. 880	7. 720	8. 880	9. 960	10. 840
44	90	66	72	72
11. 850	12. 540	13. 570	14. 220	15. 910
51	81	95	88	52
16. 680	17. 980	18. 280	19. 640	20. 690
34	28	84	96	92
21. 760	22. 810	23. 750	24. 910	25. 580
95	54	15	78	87

Exercise No. 60

Mental Multiplication

Multiply mentally by 9 the numbers in Table I on page 7.

Exercise No. 61

Mental Multiplication

Multiply mentally by 11 the numbers in Table I.

Exercise No. 62

Adding Single Columns by Pairs

Add from the bottom up.

1.	$698504.99	2.	$457012.91
	845643.09		820823.58
	761979.28		622529.46
	401349.83		715303.47
	740614.80		159363.96
	553930.31		380272.36
	896554.52		268195.94
	975160.67		789234.17
	417337.75		773286.20
	882110.35		425922.98
	116448.16		669001.18
	477406.66		502733.07
	801415.93		906396.55
	340939.01		301831.05
	380272.36		820889.23
	656958.68		548620.61
	882152.17		874185.10
	401304.99		761944.26

3. $662533.75	4. $473105.74
380277.80	141593.51
847236.82	111290.63
735356.57	897350.27
236569.58	379128.68
862061.88	966221.52
178735.81	644107.29
464385.34	104004.99
425919.44	266722.95
789249.94	987983.35
395497.48	183216.70
194426.67	295788.92
129066.25	336353.75
464347.56	578389.73
316085.34	740638.09
499498.27	236540.02
776980.14	159383.58
518437.35	729128.36

Exercise No. 63

Mental Subtraction

Raise the subtrahend to the next larger number of even dollars.

1. $83.37 — $35.72
2. $68.20 — $61.99
3. $97.48 — $17.87
4. $64.41 — $29.67

5. $25.33 — $10.65
6. $79.58 — $51.84
7. $48.54 — $20.61
8. $52.17 — $30.32

9. $91.28 — $36.82
10. $76.42 — $62.59
11. $55.30 — $18.81
12. $95.12 — $90.66

13. $65.40 — $14.93
14. $37.35 — $28.82
15. $49.01 — $21.85
16. $81.03 — $41.16

Exercise No. 64

Continuous Addition Drill

Count by 3's to 75.
Count by 4's to 100.
Count by 6's to 150.
Count by 7's to 175.
Count by 8's to 200.
Count by 9's to 225.
Count by 11's to 275.
Count by 12's to 300.

Repeat this exercise three times.

Exercise No. 65

Mental Subtraction

Do the examples in Exercise No. 63 by lowering the minuend to the next smaller number of even dollars.

Exercise No. 66

Mental Addition

Read each of these examples once, write it three times and then add it mentally from left to right.

Be careful to think of the upper number in each case as something in the thousands and not as so many hundreds. Thus in the first example the upper number should be called one thousand seven hundred forty, *not* seventeen hundred forty. It is easier to think of comparatively small numbers as hundreds rather than as thousands plus hundreds, but this method of naming leads to trouble when dealing with larger numbers, and it is best to follow one uniform system.

1. 1740	2. 1650	3. 1080	4. 1280
87	55	90	96

5. 2430	6. 2560	7. 3690	8. 1120
81	64	82	80

9. 1450	10. 1140	11. 1320	12. 1350
87	95	88	78

13. 1340	14. 1320	15. 1920	16. 2340
67	88	96	78

17. 3680	18. 1080	19. 1950	20. 2520
92	84	65	72

Exercise No. 67

Mental Subtraction

Raise the subtrahend to the next larger number of even dollars.

1. $855.30 − $8.32	9. $426.22 − $7.78
2. $844.16 − $7.29	10. $912.25 − $5.33
3. $671.46 − $4.47	11. $453.31 − $5.60
4. $834.06 − $4.09	12. $594.10 − $7.23
5. $642.02 − $7.80	13. $415.37 − $7.91
6. $836.11 − $8.68	14. $520.39 − $9.76
7. $862.21 − $4.45	15. $542.17 − $8.55
8. $532.13 − $4.41	16. $673.29 − $9.44

Exercise No. 68

Adding Single Columns by Trios

Do the examples in Exercise No. 17 on page 15 by grouping three successive numbers at a time. *Add from the top down.*

Exercise No. 69

Mental Subtraction

Do the examples in Exercise No. 67 by reducing the minuend to the next smaller number of even dollars.

Table II

Numbers for Multiplication Table Drill

A	B	C	D	E	F	G	H	J	K	L	M
2	2	2	2	2	2	2	2	2	2	2	2
4	5	6	7	8	9	10	11	8	9	10	11
6	8	10	12	14	16	18	20	14	16	18	20
8	11	14	17	3	3	3	3	20	23	3	3
10	14	3	3	9	10	11	12	13	3	11	12
12	3	7	8	15	17	19	21	9	10	19	21
14	6	11	13	4	4	4	4	15	17	4	4
3	9	15	4	10	11	12	13	21	4	12	13
5	12	4	9	16	18	20	5	4	11	20	22
7	15	8	14	5	5	5	14	10	18	5	5
9	4	12	5	11	12	13	6	16	5	13	14
11	7	16	10	17	19	6	15	22	12	21	23
13	10	5	15	6	6	14	7	5	19	6	6
	13	9	6	12	13	7	16	11	6	14	15
		13	11	18	7	15	8	17	13	22	24
			16	7	14	8	17	6	20	7	7
				13	8	16	9	12	7	15	16
					15	9	18	18	14	23	25
						17	10	7	21	8	8
							19	13	8	16	17
								19	15	24	9
									22	9	18
										17	10
											19

Exercise No. 70

Multiplication Table Drill

Use Table II on this page. Multiply the numbers in Column A successively by 2, 3, 4, 5, 6, 7, 8, 9, 10, 11, and 12. Repeat this exercise three times.

Exercise No. 71

Mental Subtraction

Raise the subtrahend to the next larger number of even dollars, and raise this amount in turn to an even $100. Thus, taking the first example: $100 from $365.42 leaves $265.42; $265.42 + $11 (difference between $100 and $89) equals $276.42; $276.42 + $.27 = $276.69.

1.	$365.42 − $88.73	**9.**	$459.48 − $87.55
2.	$950.49 − $94.98	**10.**	$553.18 − $81.64
3.	$723.67 − $40.77	**11.**	$416.07 − $29.19
4.	$614.15 − $93.79	**12.**	$426.22 − $95.78
5.	$858.51 − $84.72	**13.**	$912.25 − $33.63
6.	$928.36 − $36.82	**14.**	$753.46 − $56.57
7.	$413.54 − $86.61	**15.**	$831.05 − $60.85
8.	$342.21 − $96.62	**16.**	$743.16 − $68.29

Exercise No. 72

Adding Single Columns by Trios

Do the examples in Exercise No. 22 on page 20 by grouping three successive numbers at a time. *Add from the bottom up.*

Table III

Numbers to Be Multiplied

1.	111315	**6.**	171922	**11.**	222572
2.	111417	**7.**	182123	**12.**	541418
3.	121416	**8.**	897254	**13.**	192389
4.	121518	**9.**	248963	**14.**	151924
5.	541316	**10.**	258163	**15.**	212481

Exercise No. 73
Written Multiplication
Multiply the numbers in Table III by 6789.

Exercise No. 74
Mental Addition
Read each of the following examples once, write it three times and then add it mentally from left to right.

Think of the upper number in each case as being in the thousands and not the hundreds.

The first example would be added: 1280, 1480, 1536. In other words, take the first number as a whole, and then add to it successively the hundreds, tens and units of the second number.

1. 1280	2. 4410	3. 1960	4. 1380
256	196	686	115

5. 4620	6. 3060	7. 6510	8. 4150
693	170	837	664

9. 4080	10. 1110	11. 6480	12. 1450
204	185	144	174

13. 1640	14. 3350	15. 5150	16. 3510
246	268	344	351

17. 3040	18. 8080	19. 1240	20. 2250
304	528	372	405

Exercise No. 75

Mental Subtraction

Do the examples in Exercise No. 71 on page 49 by lowering the minuend. Reduce it to the next smaller number of even dollars. Taking the first example: $300 − $88.73 leaves $211.27; $211.27 + $65 = $276.27; $276.27 + $.42 = $276.69.

Exercise No. 76

Adding Single Columns by Trios

Do the examples in Exercise No. 26 on page 23 by grouping three successive numbers at a time. *Add from the top down.*

Exercise No. 77

Mental Multiplication

Multiply mentally by 12 the numbers in Table I on page 7.

Exercise No. 78

Adding Single Columns by Trios

Do the examples in Exercise No. 34 on page 28 by grouping three successive numbers at a time.

Exercise No. 79

Mental Subtraction

Raise the subtrahend to the next larger number of even hundreds of dollars.

1. $950.49 − $498.65
2. $646.43 − $456.57
3. $520.39 − $176.42
4. $821.13 − $468.54
5. $769.14 − $580.93
6. $831.05 − $685.34
7. $821.45 − $529.48
8. $862.39 − $197.76

9. $318.32 − $181.64   13. $416.07 − $219.44
10. $636.09 − $549.95   14. $640.02 − $493.79
11. $714.10 − $273.65   15. $746.14 − $159.93
12. $821.45 − $599.97   16. $752.30 − $183.81

Exercise No. 80

Mental Addition

Read each of the following examples once, write it three times and then add it mentally from left to right. The first example would be added: 16530, 17030, 17081.

1. 16530	2. 12930	3. 24920
551	431	623

4. 22080	5. 37150	6. 33650
552	743	673

7. 51780	8. 44460	9. 67340
863	741	962

10. 61810	11. 19360	12. 12160
883	242	152

13. 76960	14. 32670	15. 25380
962	363	282

16. 12690	17. 15320	18. 19620
141	766	654

19. 21720	20. 46650	21. 44160
543	933	736

Exercise No. 81

Written Multiplication

Multiply by 1112 each of the numbers in Table III on page 49. Wherever there occurs in the multiplicand a pair of figures that may be considered as 11 or 12, make one multiplication of this instead of two, and accordingly write down two figures in the partial product. Taking the first example:

$$
\begin{array}{r}
111315 \\
1112 \\
\hline
1335780 \\
1224465 \\
\hline
123782280
\end{array}
$$

111315 is successively multiplied (from right to left) by 12 and 11 thus: $5 \times 12 = 60$, write 0 and carry 6; $1 \times 12 = 12$, $12 + 6 = 18$, write 8 and carry 1; $3 \times 12 = 36$, $36 + 1 = 37$, write 7 and carry 3; $11 \times 12 = 132$, $132 + 3 = 135$, write 35 and carry 1; $1 \times 12 = 12$, $12 + 1 = 13$, write 13. Multiplication by 11 is carried out in the same way.

In doing these examples be watchful about placing the second partial product *two* places to the left of the first.

Exercise No. 82

Adding Single Columns by Trios

Do the examples in Exercise No. 38 on page 32 by grouping three successive numbers at a time. *Add from the bottom up.*

Exercise No. 83

Mental Subtraction

Do the examples in Exercise No. 79 on page 51 by lowering the minuend to the next smaller number of even hundreds of dollars.

Exercise No. 84

Mental Addition

Read each of the following examples once, write it three times and then add it mentally from left to right.

Add in turn the thousands, hundreds, tens and units to the upper number. In doing the first example you should say to yourself something like the following: 18360 + 1224, 19360; 19360 + 224, 19560; 19560 + 24, 19584.

1. 18360	2. 21630	3. 24960
1224	2163	3328

4. 18820	5. 16260	6. 19530
5646	1084	1953

7. 21360	8. 16420	9. 18640
2848	4926	6524

10. 10290	11. 13530	12. 16860
2401	3608	5058

13. 29240	14. 33680	15. 28590
1462	2526	4765

16. 13230	17. 26520	18. 28840
3969	1326	2163

19. 24960	20. 28290	21. 14120
4160	5658	2118

Exercise No. 85

Continuous Addition Drill

Count by 4's to 100.
Count by 6's to 150.
Count by 7's to 175.
Count by 8's to 200.
Count by 9's to 225.
Count by 11's to 275.
Count by 12's to 300.
Count by 13's to 325.

Repeat this exercise three times.

Exercise No. 86

Adding Single Columns by Trios

Do the examples in Exercise No. 41 on page 34 by grouping three successive numbers at a time. *Add from the top down.*

Exercise No. 87

Factoring

When numbers are multiplied together, they are considered *factors* of the resulting *product*. Thus 2 and 3 are factors of 6, and 3 and 5 are factors of 15.

Factoring a number is the process of resolving the number into the factors that will produce the number when multiplied together. Thus 36 may be factored as 2×18, or as 3×12, or as 4×9, or as 6×6.*

Any number that can be resolved into factors is called a *composite* number.

A *prime* number is one that has no factors besides itself and 1. Thus, 1, 2, 3, 5, 7, 11, 13, etc. are prime numbers.

---

* If it were required to give the *prime* factors of 36, these would be $2 \times 2 \times 3 \times 3$, but factoring into prime numbers has nothing to do with the purposes of this book.

On the pages starting with 146 will be found a table which analyzes all prime and composite numbers up to 625. You will be taught gradually to familiarize yourself with this entire table. The purpose of this is to help you to recognize quickly the character of these numbers—to enable you to multiply rapidly the factors that produce any of them, or to separate any of them into such factors.

Of special importance in this table are the numbers printed in italic type, since these can be produced by two factors each of which is 25 or less.

It is quite commonly appreciated that very small numbers have a definite individuality which grows out of the many associations built up around them in our minds. The individual character of higher numbers becomes similarly apparent and unforgettable when we single them out for particular attention.

For the first exercise in factoring read the first two columns of the table on page 146, and then write these from memory (or calculation) in the same form.

In studying the table note that each composite number is factored by first taking the smaller factors in the order of their size, and that the combinations are not repeated. Thus the separate ways of factoring 48 are given as 2×24, 3×16, 4×12 and 6×8. These combinations are not repeated as 8×6, 12×4, 16×3, and 24×2.

Exercise No. 88

Multiplication Table Drill

Use Table II on page 48.

Multiply the numbers in Column A successively by 3, 4, 6, 7, 8, 9, 11, 12 and 13.

Repeat this exercise three times.

This exercise takes us the first step beyond the custom-

ary limits of the multiplication table, which ordinarily goes no farther than 12 × 12. Succeeding examples will enable you to memorize the products of all pairs of numbers up to 25 × 25.

No multiplication table, as such, is presented in this book, because learning the products of higher factors by sheer power of memory is extremely difficult. On the other hand, when you are put over and over again to the necessity of figuring out these higher combinations for yourself, they soon come to stick firmly in the mind.

Exercise No. 89

Mental Addition

Read each of the following examples once, write it three times, and then add it mentally from left to right. The first example would be added: 165300, 170300, 170810.

1. 165300
    5510
	2. 129300
	    4310
		3. 249200
		    6230

4. 220800
    5520
	5. 371500
	    7430
		6. 336500
		    6730

7. 517800
    8630
	8. 444600
	    7410
		9. 673400
		    9620

10. 618100
    8830
	11. 193600
	    2420
		12. 121600
		    1520

13. 769600
    9620
	14. 326700
	    3630
		15. 253800
		    2820

16.	126900	17.	153200	18.	196200
	1410		7660		6540

19.	217200	20.	456500	21.	441600
	5430		9330		7360

Exercise No. 90
Mental Multiplication

Multiply mentally by 13 the numbers in Table I on page 7.

In working with numbers from 80 upward, immediately name 1000 as the first part of the product. Thus 83 × 13 is 1040, (+39) 1079; 97 × 13 is 1170, 1261.

Exercise No. 91
Adding Single Columns by Trios

Do the examples in Exercise No. 48 on page 39 by grouping three successive numbers at a time. *Add from the bottom up.*

Exercise No. 92
Factoring

Read the table on page 146 from 31 to 72 inclusive, and then write it in the same form.

Exercise No. 93
Mental Addition

Read each of the following examples once, write it three times and then add it mentally from left to right.

Add in turn the tens of thousands, thousands, hundreds and tens to the upper number. The first example would be added: 183600, 193600, 195600, 195840.

1. 183600	2. 216300	3. 249600
12240	21630	33280
4. 188200	5. 162600	6. 195300
56460	10840	19530
7. 213600	8. 164200	9. 186400
28480	49260	65240
10. 102900	11. 135300	12. 168600
24010	36080	50580
13. 292400	14. 336800	15. 285900
14620	25260	47650
16. 132300	17. 265200	18. 288400
39690	13260	21630
19. 249600	20. 282900	21. 141200
41600	56580	21180

Exercise No. 94

Written Multiplication

Multiply by 1213 each of the numbers in Table III on page 49. Wherever there occurs in the multiplicand a pair of figures that may be considered as 11, 12 or 13, make one multiplication of this instead of two, and write two figures in the partial product. Thus, taking the first example, we successively multiply 15, 13 and 11 by 13 and again by 12. The partial products are accordingly written in two lines instead of the customary four.

Exercise No. 95

Adding Single Columns by Trios

Do the examples in Exercise No. 54 on page 41 by grouping three successive numbers at a time. *Add from the top down.*

Exercise No. 96

Factoring

Factor the numbers from 54 to 92 inclusive in the form shown in the table on page 146.

Exercise No. 97

Mental Addition

Read each of the following examples once, write it three times and then add it mentally from left to right.

Add the whole of the second number to the first before considering the third. Repeat to yourself several times the sum of the first and second if you find this necessary.

The third example would be added: 36300, 39300, 39930; (repeat 39930, 39930); 39930, 40030, 40051.

1. 10100	2. 22200	3. 36300
1010	2220	3630
101	222	121
4. 52400	5. 70500	6. 90600
5240	7050	1510
262	141	302
7. 19100	8. 20200	9. 33300
9950	1010	2220
382	101	222

10. 48400	11. 65500	12. 84600
3630	5240	7050
121	262	141

13. 18100	14. 38200	15. 20200
7240	9050	4040
181	905	202

16. 42400	17. 66600	18. 40400
6360	8880	4040
424	666	404

19. 33600	20. 88800	21. 30300
3360	8880	9090
336	222	303

Exercise No. 98
Continuous Addition Drill

Count by 6's to 150.
Count by 7's to 175.
Count by 8's to 200.
Count by 9's to 225.
Count by 11's to 275.
Count by 12's to 300.
Count by 13's to 325.
Count by 14's to 350.

Repeat this exercise three times.

Exercise No. 99

Adding Single Columns by Trios

Do the examples in Exercise No. 62 on page 44 by grouping three successive numbers at a time. *Add from the bottom up.*

Exercise No. 100

Factoring

Factor the numbers from 73 to 111 inclusive in the form shown in the table on page 146.

Exercise No. 101

Mental Addition

Read each of the following examples once, write it three times and then add it mentally from left to right.

The first example would be added: 26200, 33200, 34000, 34060; 34060, 36060, 36156.

1. 26200	**2.** 48400	**3.** 69900
7860	9680	9320
2096	1210	1398
4. 12100	**5.** 26400	**6.** 42900
9680	9240	8580
1089	1056	1144
7. 61600	**8.** 82500	**9.** 88000
9240	9900	8800
1078	1155	1056
10. 93500	**11.** 98000	**12.** 73200
9350	9800	9760
1122	1188	1098
13. 93100	**14.** 97600	**15.** 71000
9310	9760	7100
1064	1220	1065
16. 46600	**17.** 57700	**18.** 68800
9320	5770	6880
1398	2308	2064

19. 79900	20. 24600	21. 70200
7990	9840	9320
3196	1107	1170

Exercise No. 102

Multiplication Table Drill

Use Table II on page 48.

Multiply the numbers in Column A successively by 4, 6, 7, 8, 9, 11, 12, 13 and 14.

Repeat this exercise three times.

Exercise No. 103

Two-Column Addition

You are now ready to start adding two columns at a time. Take Exercise No. 13 on page 11. *Add from the top down.*

Two-column addition is simply an application of the left-to-right methods which you have already learned. To illustrate with the first example:

$$43$$
$$62$$
$$78$$
$$81$$
$$14$$
$$\underline{87}$$

This would be added: 43, 103, 105, 175, 183, 263, 264, 274, 278, 358, 365. These are the actual steps, but with practice you will read this as 105, 183, 264, 278, 365.

Exercise No. 104

Factoring

Factor the numbers from 93 to 129 inclusive in the form shown in the table on pages 146 and 147.

Exercise No. 105

Mental Addition

Read each of the following examples once, write it three times, and then add it mentally from left to right.

1. 112700		**2.** 136800		**3.** 162900	
3220		5130		2400	
161		342		181	
4. 105700		**5.** 128800		**6.** 153900	
1510		3220		5130	
302		161		342	
7. 151200		**8.** 183400		**9.** 176400	
5040		7860		5040	
756		262		252	
10. 209600		**11.** 104800		**12.** 103200	
7860		5240		6880	
524		524		860	
13. 114100		**14.** 112800		**15.** 126000	
6520		7050		7560	
978		423		756	
16. 111000		**17.** 104400		**18.** 135900	
9250		8700		9060	
740		870		302	
19. 112800		**20.** 130500		**21.** 136800	
9870		8700		6800	
141		435		684	

Exercise No. 106

Mental Multiplication

Multiply mentally by 14 the numbers in Table I on page 7.

Exercise No. 107

Two-Column Addition

Do the examples in Exercise No. 17 on page 15 by adding two columns at a time. *Add from the bottom up.*

Exercise No. 108

Factoring

Factor the numbers from 112 to 145 inclusive in the form shown in the table on pages 146 and 147.

Exercise No. 109

Mental Addition

Read each of the following examples once, write it three times, and then add it mentally from left to right.

1. 121000 14520 484	**2.** 217600 10880 544	**3.** 253800 14100 846
4. 116000 11600 464	**5.** 145200 14520 726	**6.** 224800 10880 816
7. 171500 24010 343	**8.** 211800 10590 706	**9.** 344700 22980 383
10. 129200 16150 323	**11.** 166500 19980 666	**12.** 290400 14520 363

13.	335700	14.	272400	15.	324800
	18650		18160		23200
	746		454		928

16.	124200	17.	317800	18.	371200
	20700		18160		23200
	828		454		924

19.	395500	20.	210000	21.	540800
	34200		36750		33800
	565		525		676

Exercise No. 110
Written Multiplication

Multiply by 1314 the numbers in Table III on page 49.

Exercise No. 111
Two-Column Addition

Do the examples in Exercise No. 26 on page 23 by adding two columns at a time. *Add from the top down.*

Exercise No. 112
Factoring

Factor the numbers from 130 to 162 inclusive in the form shown in the table on page 147.

Exercise No. 113
Mental Addition

Read each of the following examples once, write it three times, and then add it mentally from left to right.

1.	123200	2.	187800	3.	254400
	39800		37560		44520
	1232		1878		2544

4. 323000
51680
3230

5. 393600
59040
3936

6. 466200
26640
4662

7. 616200
41160
1392

8. 121200
48480
2424

9. 184800
55440
3080

10. 250400
25040
3956

11. 318000
31800
4452

12. 387600
38760
1292

13. 439200
43920
1312

14. 532800
53280
1998

15. 608400
60840
2704

16. 139200
34800
1392

17. 143400
28680
1434

18. 218700
36350
2187

19. 294800
44220
2948

20. 373500
52290
3735

21. 454200
60560
4542

Exercise No. 114

Continuous Addition Drill

Count by 7's to 175.
Count by 8's to 200.
Count by 9's to 225.
Count by 11's to 275.
Count by 12's to 300.
Count by 13's to 325.

Count by 14's to 350.

Count by 15's to 375.

Repeat this exercise three times.

Exercise No. 115

Two-Column Addition

Do the examples in Exercise No. 34 on page 28 by adding two columns at a time. *Add from the bottom up.*

Exercise No. 116

Multiplication Table Drill

Use Table II on page 48.

Multiply the numbers in Column B successively by 6, 7, 8, 9, 11, 12, 13, 14 and 15.

Repeat this exercise three times.

Exercise No. 117

Factoring

Factor the numbers from 146 to 179 inclusive in the form shown in the table on page 147.

Exercise No. 118

Two-Column Addition

Do the examples in Exercise No. 38 on page 32 by adding two columns at a time. *Add from the top down.*

It slows up addition by two columns to keep repeating the number of hundreds as you go along. A good plan is to keep tally of the number of hundreds with a pencil. In all addition of long columns write numbers to be carried either at the head of the next column or beneath the figures in the total as you set them down. When looking for errors in addition, add in the opposite direction from that in which the addition was originally performed.

Exercise No. 119

Mental Multiplication

Multiply mentally by 15 the numbers in Table I on page 7.

Exercise No. 120

Two-Column Addition

Do the examples in Exercise No. 41 on page 34 by adding two columns at a time. *Add from the bottom up.*

Exercise No. 121

Factoring

Factor the numbers from 163 to 194 inclusive in the form shown in the table on page 147.

Exercise No. 122

Two-Column Addition

Do the examples in Exercise No. 48 on page 39 by adding two columns at a time. *Add from the top down.*

Exercise No. 123

Written Multiplication

Multiply by 1415 the numbers in Table III on page 49.

Exercise No. 124

Two-Column Addition

Do the examples in Exercise No. 54 on page 41 by adding two columns at a time. *Add from the bottom up.*

Exercise No. 125
Factoring

Factor the numbers from 180 to 209 inclusive in the form shown in the table on page 147.

Exercise No. 126
Two-Column Addition

Do the examples in Exercise No. 62 on page 44 by adding two columns at a time. *Add from the top down.*

Exercise No. 127
Continuous Addition Drill
Count by 8's to 200.
Count by 9's to 225.
Count by 11's to 275.
Count by 12's to 300.
Count by 13's to 325.
Count by 14's to 350.
Count by 15's to 375.
Count by 16's to 400.
Repeat this exercise three times.

Exercise No. 128
Three-Column Addition
With the practice you have had in two-column addition you should now be able to add three columns at a time. Try this with the examples in Exercise No. 38 on page 32. No additional exercises in three-column addition are given, but you can of course practice it on your own account if you so desire.

Exercise No. 129
Multiplication Table Drill
Use Table II on page 48.

Multiply the numbers in Column C successively by 7, 8, 9, 11, 12, 13, 14, 15 and 16.

Repeat this exercise three times.

Exercise No. 130
Factoring
Factor the numbers from 195 to 224 inclusive in the form shown in the table on pages 147 and 148.

Exercise No. 131
Mental Multiplication
Multiply mentally by 16 the numbers in Table I on page 7 .

Exercise No. 132
Written Multiplication
Multiply by 1516 the numbers in Table III on page 49.

Exercise No. 133
Factoring
Factor the numbers from 210 to 239 inclusive in the form shown in the table on pages 147 and 148.

DIVISION IN GENERAL

Division is multiplication in reverse. As you improve in multiplication you automatically develop your skill at division. For this reason it has been considered unnecessary to include any exercises in long division.

Exercises, however, are given in mental division, in order to round out your general calculating ability. These exercises are of the following types:

First you use the numbers from 2 to 25 as direct divisors, securing quotients from 1 to 99. Then you divide by the numbers from 2 to 9, finding answers of three places. Again, you divide by three-place numbers to arrive at quotients of one figure plus a remainder; the remainder is included so that the answer cannot be guessed but must be calculated accurately. Finally, you divide by numbers of two places and get results of two places. As division is somewhat more complicated, the exercises in division are not carried so far as those in multiplication.

Exercise No. 134

Mental Division

Divide mentally by 2 the answers to Exercise No. 45 as given on pages 161 and 162. Compare your answers with Table I on page 7.

Exercise No. 135

Continuous Addition Drill

Count by 9's to 225.

Count by 11's to 275.

Count by 12's to 300.

Count by 13's to 325.

Count by 14's to 350.

Count by 15's to 375.

Count by 16's to 400.

Count by 17's to 425.

Repeat this exercise three times.

Exercise No. 136
Mental Division

Divide mentally by 3 the answers to Exercise No. 46 as given on page 162. Compare your answers with Table I on page 7.

Exercise No. 137
Multiplication Table Drill

Use Table II on page 48.

Multiply mentally the numbers in Column D by 8, 9, 11, 12, 13, 14, 15, 16 and 17.

Repeat this exercise three times.

Exercise No. 138
Factoring

Factor the numbers from 225 to 254 inclusive in the form shown in the table on page 148.

Exercise No. 139
Mental Division

Divide mentally by 4 the answers to Exercise No. 47 as given on page 162. Compare your answers with Table I on page 7.

Exercise No. 140
Mental Multiplication

Multiply mentally by 17 the numbers in Table I on page 7.

Exercise No. 141
Written Multiplication

Multiply by 1617 the numbers in Table III on page 49. Make a single multiplication of pairs of figures in the multiplicand up to 17.

Exercise No. 142

Factoring

Factor the numbers from 240 to 269 inclusive in the form shown in the Table on page 148.

Exercise No. 143

Mental Division

Divide mentally by 5 the answers to Exercise No. 50 as given on page 163. Compare your answers with Table I on page 7 .

Exercise No. 144

Continuous Addition Drill

> Count by 11's to 275.
> Count by 12's to 300.
> Count by 13's to 325.
> Count by 14's to 350.
> Count by 15's to 375.
> Count by 16's to 400.
> Count by 17's to 425.
> Count by 18's to 450.

Repeat this exercise three times.

Exercise No. 145
Multiplication Table Drill

Use Table II on page 48.

Multiply mentally the numbers in Column E by 9, 11, 12, 13, 14, 15, 16, 17 and 18.

Repeat this exercise three times.

Exercise No. 146
Factoring

Factor the numbers from 255 to 284 inclusive in the form shown in the table on page 148.

Exercise No. 147

Mental Division

Divide mentally by 6 the answers to Exercise No. 52 as given on page 163. Compare your answers with Table I on page 7.

Exercise No. 148

Mental Multiplication

Multiply mentally by 18 the numbers in Table I on page 7.

Exercise No. 149

Written Multiplication

Multiply by 1718 the numbers in Table III on page 49. Make a single multiplication of pairs of figures in the multiplicand up to 18.

Exercise No. 150

Factoring

Factor the numbers from 270 to 299 inclusive in the form shown in the table on pages 148.

Exercise No. 151

Mental Division

Divide mentally by 7 the answers to Exercise No. 53 as given on pages 163 and 164. Compare your answers with Table I on page 7.

Exercise No. 152

Continuous Addition Drill

Count by 12's to 300.
Count by 13's to 325.
Count by 14's to 350.
Count by 15's to 375.
Count by 16's to 400.
Count by 17's to 425.
Count by 18's to 450.
Count by 19's to 475.

Repeat this exercise three times.

Exercise No. 153

Multiplication Table Drill

Use Table II on page 48.
Multiply mentally the numbers in Column F by 11, 12, 13, 14, 15, 16, 17, 18 and 19.
Repeat this exercise three times.

Exercise No. 154

Factoring

Factor the numbers from 285 to 312 inclusive in the form shown in the table on page 148.

Exercise No. 155

Mental Division

Divide mentally by 8 the answers to Exercise No. 56 as given on page 164. Compare your answers with Table I on page 7 .

Exercise No. 156

Mental Multiplication

Multiply mentally by 19 the numbers in Table I on page 7 .

Exercise No. 157

Factoring

Factor the numbers from 300 to 328 inclusive in the form shown in the table on page 148.

Exercise No. 158

Mental Division

Divide mentally by 9 the answers to Exercise No. 60 as given on page 164. Compare your answers with Table I on page 7 .

Exercise No. 159

Written Multiplication

Multiply by 1819 the numbers in Table III on page 49. Make a single multiplication of pairs of figures in the multiplicand up to 19.

Exercise No. 160

Factoring

Factor the numbers from 313 to 343 inclusive in the form shown in the table on page 149.

Exercise No. 161

Mental Division

Divide mentally by 11 the answers to Exercise No. 61 as given on page 165. Compare your answers with Table I on page 7 .

Exercise No. 162

Multiplication Table Drill

Use Table II on page 48.
Multiply mentally the numbers in Column G by 12, 13, 14, 15, 16, 17, 18, 19 and 20.

Exercise No. 163

Factoring

Factor the numbers from 329 to 359 inclusive in the form shown in the table on pages 148 and 149.

Exercise No. 164

Mental Division

Divide mentally by 12 the answers to Exercise No. 77 as given on page 166. Compare your answers with Table I on page 7.

Exercise No. 165

Mental Multiplication

Multiply mentally by 20 the numbers in Table I on page 7.

Exercise No. 166

Written Multiplication

Multiply by 1920 the numbers in Table III on page 49. Make a single multiplication of pairs of figures in the multiplicand up to 20.

Exercise No. 167

Factoring

Factor the numbers from 344 to 372 inclusive in the form shown in the table on page 149.

Exercise No. 168

Mental Division

Divide mentally by 13 the answers to Exercise No. 90 as given on page 167. Compare your answers with Table I on page 7.

Exercise No. 169

Continuous Addition Drill

Count by 13's to 325.
Count by 14's to 350.
Count by 15's to 375.
Count by 16's to 400.
Count by 17's to 425.
Count by 18's to 450.
Count by 19's to 475.
Count by 21's to 525.

Exercise No. 170

Multiplication Table Drill

Use Table II on page 48.

Multiply mentally the numbers in Column H by 12, 13, 14, 15, 16, 17, 18, 19, 20 and 21.

Exercise No. 171

Factoring

Factor the numbers from 360 to 386 inclusive in the form shown in the table on page 149.

Exercise No. 172

Mental Multiplication

Multiply mentally by 21 the numbers in Table I on page 7.

Exercise No. 173

Written Multiplication

Multiply by 2021 the numbers in Table III on page 49. Make a single multiplication of pairs of figures in the multiplicand up to 21.

Exercise No. 174

Factoring

Factor the numbers from 373 to 399 inclusive in the form shown in the table on pages 149 and 150.

Exercise No. 175

Mental Division

Divide mentally by 14 the answers to Exercise No. 106 as given on page 168. Compare your answers with Table I on page 7.

Exercise No. 176

Continuous Addition Drill

Count by 14's to 350.
Count by 15's to 375.
Count by 16's to 400.
Count by 17's to 425.
Count by 18's to 450.
Count by 19's to 475.
Count by 21's to 525.
Count by 22's to 550.

Repeat this exercise three times.

Exercise No. 177

Multiplication Table Drill

Use Table II on page 48.

Multiply mentally the numbers in Column J by 13, 14, 15, 16, 17, 18, 19, 20, 21 and 22.

Exercise No. 178

Factoring

Factor the numbers from 387 to 413 inclusive in the form shown in the table on pages 149 and 150.

Exercise No. 179

Mental Multiplication

Multiply mentally by 22 the numbers in Table I on page 7 .

Exercise No. 180

Written Multiplication

Multiply by 2122 the numbers in Table III on page 49. Make a single multiplication of pairs of figures in the multiplicand up to 22.

Exercise No. 181

Factoring

Factor the numbers from 400 to 427 inclusive in the form shown in the table on page 150 .

Exercise No. 182

Mental Division

Divide mentally by 15 the answers to Exercise No. 119 as given on page 169. Compare your answers with Table I on page 7.

Exercise No. 183

Continuous Addition Drill

Count by 15's to 375.
Count by 16's to 400.
Count by 17's to 425.
Count by 18's to 450.
Count by 19's to 475.
Count by 21's to 525.
Count by 22's to 550.
Count by 23's to 575.

Repeat this exercise three times.

Exercise No. 184

Multiplication Table Drill

Use Table II on page 48.
Multiply mentally the numbers in Column K by 14, 15, 16, 17, 18, 19, 20, 21, 22 and 23.

Exercise No. 185

Factoring

Factor the numbers from 414 to 440 inclusive in the form shown in the table on page 150.

Exercise No. 186

Mental Multiplication

Multiply mentally by 23 the numbers in Table I on page 7.

Exercise No. 187

Written Multiplication

Multiply by 2223 the numbers in Table III on page 49. Make a single multiplication of pairs of figures in the multiplicand up to 23.

Exercise No. 188

Factoring

Factor the numbers from 428 to 455 inclusive in the form shown in the table on page 150.

Exercise No. 189

Mental Division

Divide mentally by 16 the answers to Exercise No. 131 as given on pages 169 and 170. Compare your answers with Table I on page 7 .

Exercise No. 190

Continuous Addition Drill

Count by 16's to 400.
Count by 17's to 425.
Count by 18's to 450.
Count by 19's to 475.
Count by 21's to 525.
Count by 22's to 550.
Count by 23's to 575.
Count by 24's to 600.

Repeat this exercise three times.

Exercise No. 191

Multiplication Table Drill

Use Table II on page 48.

Multiply mentally the numbers in Column L by 15, 16, 17, 18, 19, 20, 21, 22, 23 and 24.

Exercise No. 192

Factoring

Factor the numbers from 441 to 467 inclusive in the form shown in the table on pages 150 and 151.

Exercise No. 193

Mental Multiplication

Multiply mentally by 24 the numbers in Table I on page 7 .

Exercise No. 194

Written Multiplication

Multiply by 2324 the numbers in Table III on page 49. Make a single multiplication of pairs of figures in the multiplicand up to 24.

Exercise No. 195

Factoring

Factor the numbers from 456 to 479 inclusive in the form shown in the table on pages 150 and 151.

Exercise No. 196

Mental Division

Divide mentally by 17 the answers to Exercise No. 140 as given on page 170. Compare your answers with Table I on page 7 .

Exercise No. 197

Continuous Addition Drill

Count by 17's to 425.
Count by 18's to 450.
Count by 19's to 475.

Count by 21's to 525.
Count by 22's to 550.
Count by 23's to 575.
Count by 24's to 600.
Count by 25's to 625.
Repeat this exercise three times.

Exercise No. 198

Multiplication Table Drill

Use Table II on page 48.
Multiply mentally the numbers in Column M by 16, 17, 18, 19, 20, 21, 22, 23, 24 and 25.

Exercise No. 199

Factoring

Factor the numbers from 468 to 491 inclusive in the form shown in the table on page 151.

Exercise No. 200

Mental Multiplication

Multiply mentally by 25 the numbers in Table I on page 7.

Exercise No. 201

Written Multiplication

Multiply by 2425 the numbers in Table III on page 49. Make a single multiplication of pairs of figures in the multiplicand up to 25.

Exercise No. 202

Factoring

Factor the numbers from 480 to 503 inclusive in the form shown in the table on page 151.

Exercise No. 203
Mental Division
Divide mentally by 18 the answers to Exercise No. 148 as given on page 170 and 171. Compare your answers with Table I on page 7 .

Exercise No. 204
Mental Multiplication
Multiply mentally by 20 the numbers in Table I on page 7 .

Exercise No. 205
Continuous Addition Drill
Count by 18's to 450.
Count by 19's to 475.
Count by 21's to 525.
Count by 22's to 550.
Count by 23's to 575.
Count by 24's to 600.
Count by 25's to 625.
Repeat this exercise three times.

Exercise No. 206
Factoring
Factor the numbers from 492 to 515 inclusive in the form shown in the table on page 151.

Exercise No. 207
Continuous Addition Drill
Count by 19's to 475.
Count by 21's to 525.
Count by 22's to 550.
Count by 23's to 575.
Count by 24's to 600.
Count by 25's to 625.
Repeat this exercise three times.

Exercise No. 208
Mental Multiplication

Multiply mentally by 30 the numbers in Table I on page 7 .

Exercise No. 209
Factoring

Factor the numbers from 504 to 527 inclusive in the form shown in the table on page 151.

Exercise No. 210
Mental Division

Divide mentally by 19 the answers to Exercise No. 149 as given on page 171. Compare your answers with Table I on page 7 .

Exercise No. 211
Continuous Addition Drill

Count by 21's to 525.
Count by 22's to 550.
Count by 23's to 575.
Count by 24's to 600.
Count by 25's to 625.

Repeat this exercise three times.

Exercise No. 212
Mental Multiplication

Multiply mentally by 40 the numbers in Table I on page 7 .

Exercise No. 213
Factoring

Factor the numbers from 516 to 539 inclusive in the form shown in the table on page 151.

Exercise No. 214
Continuous Addition Drill
Count by 22's to 550.
Count by 23's to 575.
Count by 24's to 600.
Count by 25's to 625.
Repeat this exercise three times.

Exercise No. 215
Mental Multiplication
Multiply mentally by 50 the numbers in Table I on page 7.

Exercise No. 216
Factoring
Factor the numbers from 528 to 551 inclusive in the form shown in the table on pages 151 and 152.

Exercise No. 217
Continuous Addition Drill
Count by 23's to 575.
Count by 24's to 600.
Count by 25's to 625.
Repeat this exercise three times.

Exercise No. 218
Mental Division
Divide mentally by 20 the answers to Exercise No. 165 as given on page 172. Compare your answers with Table I on page 7.

Exercise No. 219
Mental Multiplication

Multiply mentally by 60 the numbers in Table I on page 7.

Exercise No. 220
Factoring

Factor the numbers from 540 to 564 inclusive in the form shown in the table on page 152.

Exercise No. 221
Continuous Addition Drill

Count by 24's to 600.
Count by 25's to 625.

Repeat this exercise three times.

Exercise No. 222
Mental Multiplication

Multiply mentally by 70 the numbers in Table I on page 7.

Exercise No. 223
Factoring

Factor the numbers from 552 to 576 inclusive in the form shown in the table on page 152.

Exercise No. 224
Mental Division

Divide mentally by 21 the answers to Exercise No. 172 as given on page 172. Compare your answers with Table I on page 7.

Exercise No. 225
Continuous Addition Drill
Count by 25's to 625.

Repeat this exercise three times.

Exercise No. 226
Mental Multiplication
Multiply mentally by 80 the numbers in Table I on page 7 .

Exercise No. 227
Factoring
Factor the numbers from 565 to 592 inclusive in the form shown in the table on page 152.

Exercise No. 228
Mental Multiplication
Multiply mentally by 90 the numbers in Table I on page 7 .

Exercise No. 229
Multiplying Three Figures by One
We are now ready to start the mental multiplication of numbers of three places by numbers of one place. Work from left to right. Immediately name the first partial product as hundreds or thousands. Thus, taking the fourth example, this would be calculated as 800, 900, 902. The fifth example would be figured as 1000, 1120, 1124.

When dealing with numbers in the thousands be sure to consider the thousands as such and not as so many hundreds. If you wish, however, you may shorten the terminology. You may, for instance, think of one thousand one

hundred twenty-six simply as one, one twenty-six, or as one, one two six.

Perform mentally the following multiplications.

1. 121 × 2	**8.** 842 × 2	**15.** 663 × 2
2. 232 × 2	**9.** 953 × 2	**16.** 721 × 2
3. 343 × 2	**10.** 161 × 2	**17.** 832 × 2
4. 451 × 2	**11.** 222 × 2	**18.** 943 × 2
5. 562 × 2	**12.** 333 × 2	**19.** 151 × 2
6. 623 × 2	**13.** 441 × 2	**20.** 262 × 2
7. 731 × 2	**14.** 552 × 2	

Exercise No. 230

Factoring

Factor the numbers from 577 to 605 inclusive in the form shown in the table on page 152.

Exercise No. 231

Mental Division

Divide mentally by 22 the answers to Exercise No. 179 as given on page 173. Compare your answers with Table I on page 7 .

Exercise No. 232

Mental Multiplication

Multiply mentally by 110 the numbers in Table I on page 7 .

Exercise No. 233

Multiplying Three Figures by One

Perform mentally the following multiplications.

1. 131 × 3	**3.** 353 × 3	**5.** 571 × 3
2. 242 × 3	**4.** 464 × 3	**6.** 632 × 3

7. 743 × 3

8. 854 × 3

9. 961 × 3

10. 172 × 3

11. 233 × 3

12. 344 × 3

13. 451 × 3

14. 562 × 3

15. 673 × 3

16. 734 × 3

17. 841 × 3

18. 952 × 3

19. 163 × 3

20. 274 × 3

Exercise No. 234
Factoring

Factor the numbers from 593 to 625 inclusive in the form shown in the table on pages 152 and 153.

Exercise No. 235
Mental Division

Divide mentally by 23 the answers to Exercise No. 186 as given on pages 173 and 174. Compare your answers with Table I on page 7.

Exercise No. 236
Mental Multiplication

Multiply mentally by 120 the numbers in Table I on page 7.

Exercise No. 237
Multiplying Three Figures by One

Perform mentally the following multiplications.

1. 141 × 4

2. 252 × 4

3. 363 × 4

4. 474 × 4

5. 585 × 4

6. 641 × 4

7. 752 × 4

8. 863 × 4

9. 974 × 4

10. 185 × 4

11. 241 × 4

12. 352 × 4

13. 463 × 4

14. 574 × 4

15. 685 × 4

16. 741 × 4

17. 852 × 4

18. 963 × 4

19. 174 × 4

20. 285 × 4

Exercise No. 238
Mental Division

Divide mentally by 24 the answers to Exercise No. 193 as given on page 174. Compare your answers with Table I on page 7.

Exercise No. 239
Mental Multiplication

Multiply mentally by 130 the numbers in Table I on page 7.

Exercise No. 240
Multiplying Three Figures by One

Perform mentally the following multiplications.

1. 151 × 5	**8.** 872 × 5	**15.** 693 × 5
2. 262 × 5	**9.** 983 × 5	**16.** 754 × 5
3. 373 × 5	**10.** 194 × 5	**17.** 865 × 5
4. 484 × 5	**11.** 255 × 5	**18.** 976 × 5
5. 595 × 5	**12.** 366 × 5	**19.** 181 × 5
6. 656 × 5	**13.** 471 × 5	**20.** 292 × 5
7. 761 × 5	**14.** 582 × 5	

Exercise No. 241
Mental Division

Divide mentally by 25 the answers to Exercise No. 200 as given on pages 174 and 175. Compare your answers with Table I on page 7.

Exercise No. 242
Mental Multiplication

Multiply mentally by 140 the numbers in Table I on page 7.

Exercise No. 243
Multiplying Three Figures by One
Perform mentally the following multiplications.

1. 141 × 6	8. 851 × 6	15. 661 × 6
2. 252 × 6	9. 962 × 6	16. 772 × 6
3. 363 × 6	10. 173 × 6	17. 883 × 6
4. 474 × 6	11. 284 × 6	18. 994 × 6
5. 585 × 6	12. 395 × 6	19. 145 × 6
6. 696 × 6	13. 446 × 6	20. 256 × 6
7. 747 × 6	14. 557 × 6	

Exercise No. 244
Mental Multiplication
Multiply mentally by 150 the numbers in Table I on page 7.

Exercise No. 245
Multiplying Three Figures by One
Perform mentally the following multiplications.

1. 131 × 7	8. 838 × 7	15. 637 × 7
2. 242 × 7	9. 941 × 7	16. 748 × 7
3. 353 × 7	10. 152 × 7	17. 851 × 7
4. 464 × 7	11. 263 × 7	18. 962 × 7
5. 575 × 7	12. 374 × 7	19. 173 × 7
6. 686 × 7	13. 485 × 7	20. 284 × 7
7. 797 × 7	14. 596 × 7	

Exercise No. 246
Mental Multiplication
Multiply mentally by 160 the numbers in Table I on page 7.

Exercise No. 247
Multiplying Three Figures by One
Perform mentally the following multiplications.

1. 141 × 8	8. 858 × 8	15. 666 × 8
2. 252 × 8	9. 969 × 8	16. 777 × 8
3. 363 × 8	10. 171 × 8	17. 888 × 8
4. 474 × 8	11. 282 × 8	18. 999 × 8
5. 585 × 8	12. 393 × 8	19. 741 × 8
6. 696 × 8	13. 444 × 8	20. 652 × 8
7. 747 × 8	14. 555 × 8	

FRACTIONS IN GENERAL

The multiplication or the division of fractions will present no difficulty to the student of these pages since it is simply a matter of combining operations in which he is well practised.

What needs more particular attention is the addition and subtraction of the kinds of fractions most commonly encountered in practical work in office, shop and home. The average person would immediately reach for a pencil if asked the sum of $\frac{3}{4}$ and $\frac{5}{8}$ or the difference between $1\frac{1}{3}$ and $\frac{3}{8}$. Yet a little practice with calculations of this kind makes it very easy to perform them mentally.

The succeeding examples in addition and subtraction of fractions are based on the possible combinations of two fractions of the orders of halves, quarters, eighths, sixteenths, thirds, sixths, twelfths, fifths and tenths.

These exercises are to stimulate memory and rapid thinking. No instructions are given as to how to perform them because it is assumed that the student is familiar with the reduction of fractions to a common denominator.

Exercise No. 248
Reduction of Fractions

1. Reduce to eighths: $\frac{1}{2}, \frac{1}{4}, \frac{3}{4}$
2. Reduce to sixteenths: $\frac{1}{8}, \frac{1}{4}, \frac{3}{8}, \frac{1}{2}, \frac{5}{8}, \frac{3}{4}, \frac{7}{8}$
3. Reduce to sixths: $\frac{1}{3}, \frac{1}{2}, \frac{2}{3}$
4. Reduce to twelfths: $\frac{1}{6}, \frac{1}{4}, \frac{1}{3}, \frac{1}{2}, \frac{2}{3}, \frac{3}{4}, \frac{5}{6}$
5. Reduce to twenty-fourths: $\frac{1}{12}, \frac{1}{8}, \frac{1}{6}, \frac{1}{4}, \frac{1}{3}, \frac{5}{12}, \frac{1}{2}, \frac{7}{12}, \frac{5}{8}, \frac{2}{3}, \frac{3}{4}, \frac{5}{6}, \frac{11}{12}$
6. Reduce to tenths: $\frac{1}{5}, \frac{2}{5}, \frac{1}{2}, \frac{3}{5}, \frac{4}{5}$

7. Reduce to twentieths: $\frac{1}{10}$, $\frac{1}{5}$, $\frac{3}{10}$, $\frac{2}{5}$, $\frac{1}{2}$, $\frac{3}{5}$, $\frac{7}{10}$, $\frac{4}{5}$, $\frac{9}{10}$

8. Reduce to fortieths: $\frac{1}{10}$, $\frac{1}{8}$, $\frac{1}{5}$, $\frac{1}{4}$, $\frac{3}{10}$, $\frac{3}{8}$, $\frac{2}{5}$, $\frac{1}{2}$, $\frac{3}{5}$, $\frac{5}{8}$, $\frac{7}{10}$, $\frac{3}{4}$, $\frac{4}{5}$, $\frac{7}{8}$, $\frac{9}{10}$

9. Reduce to fifteenths: $\frac{1}{5}$, $\frac{1}{3}$, $\frac{2}{5}$, $\frac{3}{5}$, $\frac{2}{3}$, $\frac{4}{5}$

10. Reduce to thirtieths: $\frac{1}{10}$, $\frac{1}{6}$, $\frac{1}{5}$, $\frac{3}{10}$, $\frac{1}{3}$, $\frac{2}{5}$, $\frac{1}{2}$, $\frac{3}{5}$, $\frac{2}{3}$, $\frac{7}{10}$, $\frac{4}{5}$, $\frac{5}{6}$, $\frac{9}{10}$

Exercise No. 249
Mental Multiplication

Multiply mentally by 170 the numbers in Table I on page **7**.

Exercise No. 250
Addition of Fractions

Add the following mentally.

1. $\frac{1}{2} + \frac{1}{4}$	**11.** $\frac{3}{4} + \frac{1}{8}$	**21.** $\frac{1}{2} + \frac{13}{16}$	**31.** $\frac{3}{4} + \frac{1}{16}$
2. $\frac{1}{2} + \frac{9}{4}$	**12.** $\frac{3}{4} + \frac{3}{8}$	**22.** $\frac{1}{2} + \frac{15}{16}$	**32.** $\frac{3}{4} + \frac{3}{16}$
3. $\frac{1}{2} + \frac{1}{8}$	**13.** $\frac{3}{4} + \frac{5}{8}$	**23.** $\frac{1}{4} + \frac{1}{16}$	**33.** $\frac{3}{4} + \frac{5}{16}$
4. $\frac{1}{2} + \frac{3}{8}$	**14.** $\frac{3}{4} + \frac{7}{8}$	**24.** $\frac{1}{4} + \frac{3}{16}$	**34.** $\frac{3}{4} + \frac{7}{16}$
5. $\frac{1}{2} + \frac{5}{8}$	**15.** $\frac{1}{2} + \frac{1}{16}$	**25.** $\frac{1}{4} + \frac{5}{16}$	**35.** $\frac{3}{4} + \frac{9}{16}$
6. $\frac{1}{2} + \frac{7}{8}$	**16.** $\frac{1}{2} + \frac{3}{16}$	**26.** $\frac{1}{4} + \frac{7}{16}$	**36.** $\frac{3}{4} + \frac{11}{16}$
7. $\frac{1}{4} + \frac{1}{8}$	**17.** $\frac{1}{2} + \frac{5}{16}$	**27.** $\frac{1}{4} + \frac{9}{16}$	**37.** $\frac{3}{4} + \frac{13}{16}$
8. $\frac{1}{4} + \frac{3}{8}$	**18.** $\frac{1}{2} + \frac{7}{16}$	**28.** $\frac{1}{4} + \frac{11}{16}$	**38.** $\frac{3}{4} + \frac{15}{16}$
9. $\frac{1}{4} + \frac{5}{8}$	**19.** $\frac{1}{2} + \frac{9}{16}$	**29.** $\frac{1}{4} + \frac{13}{16}$	**39.** $\frac{1}{8} + \frac{1}{16}$
10. $\frac{1}{4} + \frac{7}{8}$	**20.** $\frac{1}{2} + \frac{11}{16}$	**30.** $\frac{1}{4} + \frac{15}{16}$	**40.** $\frac{1}{8} + \frac{3}{16}$

Exercise No. 251
Multiplying Three Figures by One

1. 152×9	**8.** 869×9	**15.** 679×9
2. 263×9	**9.** 973×9	**16.** 784×9
3. 374×9	**10.** 184×9	**17.** 895×9
4. 485×9	**11.** 295×9	**18.** 946×9
5. 596×9	**12.** 346×9	**19.** 157×9
6. 647×9	**13.** 457×9	**20.** 268×9
7. 758×9	**14.** 568×9	

Exercise No. 252
Mental Division
Divide mentally by 2 the answers to Exercise No. 229 as given on page 175.

Exercise No. 253
Addition of Fractions
Do the last thirty examples in Exercise No. 250 on the preceding page, and also add the following.

1. $\frac{1}{8} + \frac{5}{16}$ 4. $\frac{1}{8} + \frac{11}{16}$ 7. $\frac{3}{8} + \frac{1}{16}$ 10. $\frac{3}{8} + \frac{7}{16}$
2. $\frac{1}{8} + \frac{7}{16}$ 5. $\frac{1}{8} + \frac{13}{16}$ 8. $\frac{3}{8} + \frac{3}{16}$
3. $\frac{1}{8} + \frac{9}{16}$ 6. $\frac{1}{8} + \frac{15}{16}$ 9. $\frac{3}{8} + \frac{5}{16}$

Exercise No. 254
Mental Multiplication
Multiply mentally by 180 the numbers in Table I on page 7.

Exercise No. 255
Mental Division
Divide mentally by 3 the answers to Exercise No. 233 as given on page 175. Compare your answers with Exercise No. 233.

Exercise No. 256
Addition of Fractions
Review the last twenty examples in Exercise No. 250 on page 97 and those in Exercise No. 253 on page 98. Also add the following.

1. $\frac{3}{8} + \frac{9}{16}$ 4. $\frac{3}{8} + \frac{15}{16}$ 7. $\frac{5}{8} + \frac{5}{16}$ 10. $\frac{5}{8} + \frac{11}{16}$
2. $\frac{3}{8} + \frac{11}{16}$ 5. $\frac{5}{8} + \frac{1}{16}$ 8. $\frac{5}{8} + \frac{7}{16}$
3. $\frac{3}{8} + \frac{13}{16}$ 6. $\frac{5}{8} + \frac{5}{16}$ 9. $\frac{5}{8} + \frac{9}{16}$

Exercise No. 257
Mental Multiplication
Multiply mentally by 190 the numbers in Table I on page 7.

Exercise No. 258
Mental Division
Divide mentally by 4 the answers to Exercise No. 237 as given on page 175.

Exercise No. 259
Addition of Fractions
Review the last ten examples in Exercise No. 250 on page 97, as well as those in Exercise No. 253 on page 98 and Exercise No. 256 on page 98. Also add the following.

1. $\frac{5}{8} + \frac{13}{16}$ 4. $\frac{7}{8} + \frac{3}{16}$ 7. $\frac{7}{8} + \frac{9}{16}$ 10. $\frac{7}{8} + \frac{15}{16}$

2. $\frac{5}{8} + \frac{15}{16}$ 5. $\frac{7}{8} + \frac{5}{16}$ 8. $\frac{7}{8} + \frac{11}{16}$

3. $\frac{7}{8} + \frac{1}{16}$ 6. $\frac{7}{8} + \frac{7}{16}$ 9. $\frac{7}{8} + \frac{13}{16}$

Exercise No. 260
Mental Multiplication
Multiply mentally by 200 the numbers in Table I on page 7.

Exercise No. 261
Addition of Fractions
Review the examples in Exercise No. 253 on page 98, No. 256 on page 98 and No. 259 above. Also add the following.

1. $\frac{1}{3} + \frac{1}{6}$ 4. $\frac{1}{3} + \frac{5}{12}$ 7. $\frac{2}{3} + \frac{1}{12}$ 10. $\frac{2}{3} + \frac{11}{12}$

2. $\frac{2}{3} + \frac{1}{6}$ 5. $\frac{1}{3} + \frac{7}{12}$ 8. $\frac{2}{3} + \frac{5}{12}$

3. $\frac{1}{3} + \frac{1}{12}$ 6. $\frac{1}{3} + \frac{11}{12}$ 9. $\frac{2}{3} + \frac{7}{12}$

Exercise No. 262
Mental Division

Divide mentally by 5 the answers to Exercise No. 240 as given on page 175.

Exercise No. 263
Subtraction of Fractions
Perform mentally the following subtractions.

1. $\frac{3}{4} - \frac{1}{2}$	8. $\frac{5}{8} - \frac{1}{4}$	16. $\frac{11}{16} - \frac{1}{2}$	24. $\frac{7}{16} - \frac{1}{4}$
2. $1\frac{1}{4} - \frac{1}{2}$	9. $\frac{7}{8} - \frac{1}{4}$	17. $\frac{13}{16} - \frac{1}{2}$	25. $\frac{9}{16} - \frac{1}{4}$
3. $\frac{5}{8} - \frac{1}{2}$	10. $1\frac{1}{8} - \frac{1}{4}$	18. $\frac{15}{16} - \frac{1}{2}$	26. $\frac{11}{16} - \frac{1}{4}$
4. $\frac{7}{8} - \frac{1}{2}$	11. $\frac{7}{8} - \frac{3}{4}$	19. $1\frac{1}{16} - \frac{1}{2}$	27. $\frac{13}{16} - \frac{1}{4}$
5. $1\frac{1}{8} - \frac{1}{2}$	12. $1\frac{1}{8} - \frac{3}{4}$	20. $1\frac{3}{16} - \frac{1}{2}$	28. $\frac{15}{16} - \frac{1}{4}$
6. $1\frac{3}{8} - \frac{1}{2}$	13. $1\frac{3}{8} - \frac{3}{4}$	21. $1\frac{5}{16} - \frac{1}{2}$	29. $1\frac{1}{16} - \frac{1}{4}$
7. $\frac{3}{8} - \frac{1}{4}$	14. $1\frac{5}{8} - \frac{3}{4}$	22. $1\frac{7}{16} - \frac{1}{2}$	30. $1\frac{3}{16} - \frac{1}{4}$
	15. $\frac{9}{16} - \frac{1}{2}$	23. $\frac{5}{16} - \frac{1}{4}$	

Exercise No. 264
Mental Multiplication
Multiply mentally by 210 the numbers in Table I on page 7 .

Exercise No. 265
Subtraction of Fractions
Review the last twenty examples in Exercise No. 263 above, and also perform the following subtractions.

1. $\frac{13}{16} - \frac{3}{4}$	4. $1\frac{3}{16} - \frac{3}{4}$	7. $1\frac{9}{16} - \frac{3}{4}$	10. $\frac{5}{16} - \frac{1}{8}$
2. $\frac{15}{16} - \frac{3}{4}$	5. $1\frac{5}{16} - \frac{3}{4}$	8. $1\frac{11}{16} - \frac{3}{4}$	
3. $1\frac{1}{16} - \frac{3}{4}$	6. $1\frac{7}{16} - \frac{3}{4}$	9. $\frac{3}{16} - \frac{1}{8}$	

Exercise No. 266
Mental Division
Divide mentally by 6 the answers to Exercise No. 243 as given on page 175.

Exercise No. 267
Addition of Fractions
Review the examples in Exercise No. 256 on page 98 , No. 259 on page 99 and No. 261 on page 99. Also perform the following additions.

1. $\frac{1}{6} + \frac{1}{12}$ 4. $\frac{1}{6} + \frac{11}{12}$ 7. $\frac{5}{6} + \frac{7}{12}$ 10. $\frac{1}{2} + \frac{2}{3}$

2. $\frac{1}{6} + \frac{5}{12}$ 5. $\frac{5}{6} + \frac{1}{12}$ 8. $\frac{5}{6} + \frac{11}{12}$

3. $\frac{1}{6} + \frac{7}{12}$ 6. $\frac{5}{6} + \frac{5}{12}$ 9. $\frac{1}{2} + \frac{1}{3}$

Exercise No. 268
Mental Multiplication
Multiply mentally by 220 the numbers in Table I on page 7 .

Exercise No. 269
Subtraction of Fractions
Review the last ten examples in Exercise No. 263 on page 100 and No. 265 on page 100. Also perform the following subtractions.

1. $\frac{7}{16} - \frac{1}{8}$ 4. $\frac{13}{16} - \frac{1}{8}$ 7. $\frac{7}{16} - \frac{3}{8}$ 10. $\frac{13}{16} - \frac{3}{8}$

2. $\frac{9}{16} - \frac{1}{8}$ 5. $\frac{15}{16} - \frac{1}{8}$ 8. $\frac{9}{16} - \frac{3}{8}$

3. $\frac{11}{16} - \frac{1}{8}$ 6. $1\frac{1}{16} - \frac{1}{8}$ 9. $\frac{11}{16} - \frac{3}{8}$

Exercise No. 270
Mental Division
Divide mentally by 7 the answers to Exercise No. 245 as given on page 176.

Exercise No. 271

Addition of Fractions

Review the examples in Exercise No. 259 on page 99 , No. 261 on page 99 and No. 267 on page 101. Also perform the following additions.

1. $\frac{1}{2} + \frac{1}{6}$ **4.** $\frac{1}{4} + \frac{5}{6}$ **7.** $\frac{1}{8} + \frac{1}{6}$ **10.** $\frac{7}{8} + \frac{1}{6}$

2. $\frac{1}{2} + \frac{5}{6}$ **5.** $\frac{3}{4} + \frac{1}{6}$ **8.** $\frac{3}{8} + \frac{1}{6}$

3. $\frac{1}{4} + \frac{1}{6}$ **6.** $\frac{3}{4} + \frac{5}{6}$ **9.** $\frac{5}{8} + \frac{1}{6}$

Exercise No. 272

Mental Multiplication

Multiply mentally by 230 the numbers in Table I on page 7 .

Exercise No. 273

Subtraction of Fractions

Review the examples in Exercise No. 265 on page 100 and No. 269 on page 101. Also perform the following subtractions.

1. $\frac{15}{16} - \frac{3}{8}$ **4.** $1\frac{5}{16} - \frac{3}{8}$ **7.** $\frac{15}{16} - \frac{5}{8}$ **10.** $1\frac{5}{16} - \frac{5}{8}$

2. $1\frac{1}{16} - \frac{3}{8}$ **5.** $\frac{11}{16} - \frac{5}{8}$ **8.** $1\frac{1}{16} - \frac{5}{8}$

3. $1\frac{3}{16} - \frac{3}{8}$ **6.** $\frac{13}{16} - \frac{5}{8}$ **9.** $1\frac{3}{16} - \frac{5}{8}$

Exercise No. 274

Mental Division

Divide mentally by 8 the answers to Exercise No. 247 as given on page 176.

Exercise No. 275

Addition of Fractions

Review the examples in Exercise No. 261 on page 99 , No. 267 on page 101 and No. 271 on this page. Also perform the following additions.

1. $\frac{1}{8} + \frac{5}{6}$ 4. $\frac{7}{8} + \frac{5}{6}$ 7. $\frac{1}{2} + \frac{7}{12}$ 10. $\frac{1}{4} + \frac{5}{12}$

2. $\frac{3}{8} + \frac{5}{6}$ 5. $\frac{1}{2} + \frac{1}{12}$ 8. $\frac{1}{2} + \frac{11}{12}$

3. $\frac{5}{8} + \frac{5}{6}$ 6. $\frac{1}{2} + \frac{5}{12}$ 9. $\frac{1}{4} + \frac{1}{12}$

Exercise No. 276
Mental Multiplication

Multiply mentally by 240 the numbers in Table I on page 7.

Exercise No. 277
Subtraction of Fractions

Review the examples in Exercise No. 269 on page 101 and No. 273 on page 102. Also perform the following.

1. $1\frac{7}{16} - \frac{5}{8}$ 4. $1\frac{1}{16} - \frac{7}{8}$ 7. $1\frac{7}{16} - \frac{7}{8}$ 10. $1\frac{13}{16} - \frac{7}{8}$

2. $1\frac{9}{16} - \frac{5}{8}$ 5. $1\frac{3}{16} - \frac{7}{8}$ 8. $1\frac{9}{16} - \frac{7}{8}$

3. $\frac{15}{16} - \frac{7}{8}$ 6. $1\frac{5}{16} - \frac{7}{8}$ 9. $1\frac{11}{16} - \frac{7}{8}$

Exercise No. 278
Mental Division

Divide mentally by 9 the answers to Exercise No. 251 as given on page 176.

Exercise No. 279
Addition of Fractions

Review the examples in Exercise No. 267 on page 101, No. 271 on page 102 and No. 275 on this page. Also perform the following additions.

1. $\frac{1}{4} + \frac{7}{12}$ 4. $\frac{3}{4} + \frac{5}{12}$ 7. $\frac{1}{8} + \frac{1}{12}$ 10. $\frac{1}{8} + \frac{11}{12}$

2. $\frac{1}{4} + \frac{11}{12}$ 5. $\frac{3}{4} + \frac{7}{12}$ 8. $\frac{1}{8} + \frac{5}{12}$

3. $\frac{3}{4} + \frac{1}{12}$ 6. $\frac{3}{4} + \frac{11}{12}$ 9. $\frac{1}{8} + \frac{7}{12}$

Exercise No. 280
Mental Multiplication
Multiply mentally by 250 the numbers in Table I on page 7 .

Exercise No. 281
Subtraction of Fractions
Review the examples in Exercise No. 273 on page 102 and No. 277 on page 103. Also perform the following subtractions.

1. $\frac{1}{2} - \frac{1}{3}$ 4. $\frac{3}{4} - \frac{1}{3}$ 7. $\frac{3}{4} - \frac{2}{3}$ 10. $1\frac{7}{12} - \frac{2}{3}$
2. $\frac{5}{6} - \frac{2}{3}$ 5. $\frac{11}{12} - \frac{1}{3}$ 8. $1\frac{1}{12} - \frac{2}{3}$
3. $\frac{5}{12} - \frac{1}{3}$ 6. $1\frac{1}{4} - \frac{1}{3}$ 9. $1\frac{1}{4} - \frac{2}{3}$

Exercise No. 282
Mental Division
Divide mentally the following. Express remainders as such instead of as fractions.

1. $328 \div 121$ 8. $1786 \div 842$ 15. $1998 \div 571$
2. $593 \div 232$ 9. $2114 \div 953$ 16. $690 \div 141$
3. $794 \div 343$ 10. $439 \div 161$ 17. $1208 \div 252$
4. $1249 \div 451$ 11. $406 \div 131$ 18. $1704 \div 363$
5. $1580 \div 562$ 12. $776 \div 242$ 19. $2178 \div 474$
6. $1835 \div 623$ 13. $1164 \div 353$ 20. $2620 \div 585$
7. $1774 \div 731$ 14. $1574 \div 464$

Exercise No. 283
Addition of Fractions
Review the examples in Exercise No. 271 on page 102, No. 275 on page 103 and No. 279 on page 103. Also perform the following additions.

1. $\frac{3}{8} + \frac{1}{12}$ 4. $\frac{3}{8} + \frac{11}{12}$ 7. $\frac{5}{8} + \frac{7}{12}$ 10. $\frac{7}{8} + \frac{5}{12}$
2. $\frac{3}{8} + \frac{5}{12}$ 5. $\frac{5}{8} + \frac{1}{12}$ 8. $\frac{5}{8} + \frac{11}{12}$
3. $\frac{3}{8} + \frac{7}{12}$ 6. $\frac{5}{8} + \frac{5}{12}$ 9. $\frac{7}{8} + \frac{1\frac{1}{12}}$

Exercise No. 284

Multiplying Two Figures by Two

With this exercise we start the general multiplication of two numbers of two places each. You have had some experience with such numbers in using the numbers up to 25 as direct multipliers. In the succeeding exercises, however, the multipliers are greater than 25 and the operation is performed differently.

Multiply the whole of the multiplicand by the first figure of the multiplier; next multiply the whole of the multiplicand by the second figure of the multiplier; and finally add the two partial products.

When you multiply the first figure of the multiplicand by the first figure of the multiplier you will get a number of either three places, as in the first example (where 20×40 produces 800), or four places, as in the second example (where 2×5 produces 10). Add to this first result as you work along from left to right. Similarly, when you multiply the first figure of the multiplicand by the second figure of the multiplier, you will get a number of either two or three places.

Repeat to yourself the original example and the partial products as often as you find necessary. The need for such repetitions will grow less as you become more practised.

Taking the first example: repeat, 41×26, 41×26, 41×26. 40×20 is 800, 1×2 is 2, 820. (say 1×2 rather than 1×20 because the former method is simpler when dealing with large numbers. When you think of the 2 as following the 8 it of course becomes a 20 in the product.) Repeat 820, 820, 820. 40×6 is 240, 1×6 is 6, 246. Repeat $820 + 246$, $820 + 246$, $820 + 246$. Add: 1020, 1060, 1066.

The second example is performed: 1000, 1020; 350, 357. $1020 + 357$, 1320, 1370, 1377.

Most of the examples in this exercise are very simple and there can be no objection to your shortening the method given, which is a general method applicable to increasingly larger numbers. Thus in the examples illustrated you should be able to note at a glance that the first partial products are 820 and 1020.

1. 41 × 26	**8.** 41 × 34	**15.** 41 × 33
2. 51 × 27	**9.** 51 × 26	**16.** 51 × 34
3. 61 × 28	**10.** 61 × 27	**17.** 61 × 26
4. 71 × 29	**11.** 71 × 28	**18.** 71 × 27
5. 81 × 31	**12.** 81 × 29	**19.** 81 × 28
6. 91 × 32	**13.** 91 × 31	**20.** 91 × 29
7. 31 × 33	**14.** 31 × 32	

Exercise No. 285
Subtraction of Fractions

Review the examples in Exercise No. 277 on page 103 and No. 281 on page 104. Also perform the following subtractions.

1. $\frac{1}{4} - \frac{1}{6}$	**4.** $1\frac{1}{12} - \frac{1}{6}$	**7.** $1\frac{5}{12} - \frac{5}{6}$	**10.** $1\frac{1}{6} - \frac{1}{2}$
2. $\frac{7}{12} - \frac{1}{6}$	**5.** $\frac{11}{12} - \frac{5}{6}$	**8.** $1\frac{3}{4} - \frac{5}{6}$	
3. $\frac{3}{4} - \frac{1}{6}$	**6.** $1\frac{1}{4} - \frac{5}{6}$	**9.** $\frac{5}{6} - \frac{1}{2}$	

Exercise No. 286
Mental Division

Divide mentally the following.

1. 445 ÷ 222	**6.** 2274 ÷ 632	**11.** 2830 ÷ 641
2. 695 ÷ 333	**7.** 2747 ÷ 743	**12.** 3233 ÷ 752
3. 1258 ÷ 441	**8.** 3242 ÷ 854	**13.** 3624 ÷ 863
4. 1655 ÷ 552	**9.** 3747 ÷ 961	**14.** 3989 ÷ 974
5. 1700 ÷ 663	**10.** 533 ÷ 172	**15.** 902 ÷ 185

16. 845 ÷ 151   **18.** 2013 ÷ 373   **20.** 3094 ÷ 595

17. 1440 ÷ 262   **19.** 2564 ÷ 484

Exercise No. 287

Addition of Fractions

Review the examples in Exercise No. 275 on page 103, No. 279 on page 103 and No. 283 on page 104. Also perform the following additions.

1. $\frac{7}{8} + \frac{7}{12}$ **4.** $\frac{1}{5} + \frac{3}{10}$ **7.** $\frac{2}{5} + \frac{1}{10}$ **10.** $\frac{2}{5} + \frac{9}{10}$

2. $\frac{7}{8} + \frac{11}{12}$ **5.** $\frac{1}{5} + \frac{7}{10}$ **8.** $\frac{2}{5} + \frac{3}{10}$

3. $\frac{1}{5} + \frac{1}{10}$ **6.** $\frac{1}{5} + \frac{9}{10}$ **9.** $\frac{2}{5} + \frac{7}{10}$

Exercise No. 288

Multiplying Two Figures by Two

In doing exercises of this type always use the second number as the multiplier. Using the first example to illustrate, find 30 times 42 and then 5 times 42; do not work the other way around by finding 40 times 35 and then 2 times 35. This caution is given because of the special way in which the exercises are graded.

1. 42 × 35   **8.** 42 × 43   **15.** 42 × 42

2. 52 × 36   **9.** 52 × 35   **16.** 52 × 43

3. 62 × 37   **10.** 62 × 36   **17.** 62 × 34

4. 72 × 38   **11.** 72 × 37   **18.** 72 × 35

5. 82 × 39   **12.** 82 × 38   **19.** 82 × 36

6. 92 × 41   **13.** 92 × 39   **20.** 92 × 37

7. 32 × 42   **14.** 32 × 41

Exercise No. 289

Subtraction of Fractions

Review the examples in Exercise No. 277 on page 103 and No. 281 on page 104. Also perform the following subtractions.

1. $\frac{2}{3} - \frac{1}{2}$ 4. $1\frac{1}{24} - \frac{1}{4}$ 7. $\frac{7}{24} - \frac{1}{8}$ 10. $1\frac{1}{24} - \frac{7}{8}$

2. $1\frac{1}{3} - \frac{1}{2}$ 5. $\frac{11}{12} - \frac{3}{4}$ 8. $\frac{13}{24} - \frac{3}{8}$

3. $\frac{5}{12} - \frac{1}{4}$ 6. $1\frac{7}{12} - \frac{3}{4}$ 9. $\frac{19}{24} - \frac{5}{8}$

Exercise No. 290
Mental Division

1. $1479 \div 721$
2. $2435 \div 832$
3. $2036 \div 943$
4. $387 \div 151$
5. $623 \div 262$
6. $745 \div 233$
7. $1134 \div 344$

8. $1523 \div 451$
9. $1966 \div 562$
10. $2421 \div 673$
11. $1156 \div 241$
12. $1643 \div 352$
13. $2128 \div 463$
14. $2581 \div 574$

15. $3012 \div 685$
16. $3347 \div 656$
17. $4498 \div 761$
18. $4924 \div 872$
19. $5547 \div 983$
20. $1067 \div 194$

Exercise No. 291
Addition of Fractions

Review the examples in Exercise No. 279 on page 103, No. 283 on page 104 and No. 287 on page 107. Also perform the following additions.

1. $\frac{3}{5} + \frac{1}{10}$ 4. $\frac{3}{5} + \frac{9}{10}$ 7. $\frac{4}{5} + \frac{7}{10}$ 10. $\frac{1}{2} + \frac{2}{5}$

2. $\frac{3}{5} + \frac{3}{10}$ 5. $\frac{4}{5} + \frac{1}{10}$ 8. $\frac{4}{5} + \frac{9}{10}$

3. $\frac{3}{5} + \frac{7}{10}$ 6. $\frac{4}{5} + \frac{3}{10}$ 9. $\frac{1}{2} + \frac{1}{5}$

Exercise No. 292
Mental Multiplication

Multiply mentally the following.

1. 43×44
2. 53×45
3. 63×46
4. 73×47
5. 83×48
6. 93×49
7. 33×51

8. 43×52
9. 53×44
10. 63×45
11. 73×46
12. 83×47
13. 93×48
14. 33×49

15. 43×51
16. 53×52
17. 63×44
18. 78×45
19. 83×46
20. 93×47

Exercise No. 293

Subtraction of Fractions

Review the examples in Exercise No. 281 on page 104
and No. 289 on page 108. Also do the following.

1. $\frac{23}{24} - \frac{1}{8}$ 4. $1\frac{17}{24} - \frac{7}{8}$ 7. $1\frac{1}{12} - \frac{1}{2}$ 10. $\frac{2}{3} - \frac{1}{4}$

2. $1\frac{5}{24} - \frac{3}{8}$ 5. $\frac{7}{12} - \frac{1}{2}$ 8. $1\frac{5}{12} - \frac{1}{2}$

3. $1\frac{11}{24} - \frac{5}{8}$ 6. $\frac{11}{12} - \frac{1}{2}$ 9. $\frac{1}{3} - \frac{1}{4}$

Exercise No. 294

Mental Division

Divide mentally the following.

1. $444 \div 131$ 8. $4716 \div 963$ 15. $3573 \div 693$

2. $795 \div 242$ 9. $815 \div 174$ 16. $971 \div 141$

3. $1154 \div 353$ 10. $1348 \div 285$ 17. $1712 \div 252$

4. $1424 \div 464$ 11. $1421 \div 255$ 18. $2255 \div 363$

5. $1767 \div 571$ 12. $2118 \div 366$ 19. $2955 \div 474$

6. $3186 \div 740$ 13. $2676 \div 471$ 20. $3820 \div 585$

7. $3493 \div 852$ 14. $3375 \div 582$

Exercise No. 295

Addition of Fractions

Review the examples in Exercise No. 279 on page 103,
No. 283 on page 104 and No. 292 on page 108. Also perform the following additions.

1. $\frac{1}{2} + \frac{3}{5}$ 4. $\frac{1}{2} + \frac{3}{10}$ 7. $\frac{1}{4} + \frac{1}{5}$ 10. $\frac{1}{4} + \frac{4}{5}$

2. $\frac{1}{2} + \frac{4}{5}$ 5. $\frac{1}{2} + \frac{7}{10}$ 8. $\frac{1}{4} + \frac{2}{5}$

3. $\frac{1}{2} + \frac{1}{10}$ 6. $\frac{1}{2} + \frac{9}{10}$ 9. $\frac{1}{4} + \frac{3}{5}$

Exercise No. 296
Mental Multiplication
Multiply mentally the following.

1. 44×53
2. 54×54
3. 64×55
4. 74×56
5. 84×57
6. 94×58
7. 34×59

8. 44×61
9. 54×53
10. 64×54
11. 74×55
12. 84×56
13. 94×57
14. 34×58

15. 44×59
16. 59×61
17. 64×53
18. 74×54
19. 84×55
20. 94×56

Exercise No. 297
Subtraction of Fractions
Review the examples in Exercise No. 289 on page 108 and No. 293 on page 109. Also perform the following subtractions.

1. $\frac{5}{6} - \frac{1}{4}$
2. $1\frac{1}{6} - \frac{1}{4}$
3. $\frac{5}{6} - \frac{3}{4}$

4. $1\frac{1}{6} - \frac{3}{4}$
5. $1\frac{1}{3} - \frac{3}{4}$
6. $1\frac{2}{3} - \frac{3}{4}$

7. $\frac{5}{24} - \frac{1}{8}$
8. $\frac{13}{24} - \frac{1}{8}$
9. $\frac{17}{24} - \frac{1}{8}$

10. $1\frac{1}{24} - \frac{1}{8}$

Exercise No. 298
Mental Division
Divide mentally the following.

1. $3989 \div 754$
2. $4967 \div 865$
3. $5192 \div 976$
4. $1002 \div 181$
5. $1566 \div 292$
6. $4486 \div 696$
7. $4632 \div 747$

8. $5206 \div 851$
9. $6381 \div 962$
10. $1153 \div 173$
11. $982 \div 131$
12. $1829 \div 242$
13. $2706 \div 353$
14. $3433 \div 464$

15. $4089 \div 575$
16. $1200 \div 141$
17. $2141 \div 252$
18. $3084 \div 363$
19. $4152 \div 474$
20. $5101 \div 585$

Exercise No. 299
Addition of Fractions

Review the examples in Exercise No. 283 on page 104, No. 292 on page 108 and No. 295 on page 109. Also perform the following additions.

1. $\frac{1}{4} + \frac{1}{10}$ 4. $\frac{1}{4} + \frac{9}{10}$ 7. $\frac{3}{4} + \frac{3}{5}$ 10. $\frac{3}{4} + \frac{3}{10}$

2. $\frac{1}{4} + \frac{3}{10}$ 5. $\frac{3}{4} + \frac{1}{5}$ 8. $\frac{3}{4} + \frac{4}{5}$

3. $\frac{1}{4} + \frac{7}{10}$ 6. $\frac{3}{4} + \frac{2}{5}$ 9. $\frac{3}{4} + \frac{1}{10}$

Exercise No. 300
Mental Multiplication

Multiply mentally the following.

1. 45×62 8. 45×69 15. 45×68
2. 55×63 9. 55×62 16. 55×69
3. 65×64 10. 65×63 17. 65×62
4. 75×65 11. 75×64 18. 75×63
5. 85×66 12. 85×65 19. 85×64
6. 95×67 13. 95×66 20. 95×65
7. 35×68 14. 35×67

Exercise No. 301
Subtraction of Fractions

Review the examples in Exercise No. 293 on page 109 and No. 297 on page 110. Also perform the following subtractions.

1. $\frac{11}{24} - \frac{3}{8}$ 4. $1\frac{7}{24} - \frac{3}{8}$ 7. $1\frac{5}{24} - \frac{5}{8}$ 10. $1\frac{7}{24} - \frac{7}{8}$

2. $\frac{19}{24} - \frac{3}{8}$ 5. $\frac{17}{24} - \frac{5}{8}$ 8. $1\frac{13}{24} - \frac{5}{8}$

3. $\frac{23}{24} - \frac{3}{8}$ 6. $1\frac{11}{24} - \frac{5}{8}$ 9. $\frac{23}{24} - \frac{7}{8}$

Exercise No. 302
Mental Division

Divide mentally the following.

1. $1714 \div 284$ 3. $2714 \div 446$ 5. $4617 \div 661$
2. $2399 \div 395$ 4. $3507 \div 557$ 6. $5303 \div 686$

7. 5886 ÷ 797   **12.** 6588 ÷ 747   **17.** 2502 ÷ 263
8. 6665 ÷ 838   **13.** 7189 ÷ 858   **18.** 3440 ÷ 374
9. 7233 ÷ 941   **14.** 8238 ÷ 969   **19.** 4450 ÷ 485
10. 1084 ÷ 152   **15.** 1385 ÷ 171   **20.** 5423 ÷ 596
11. 5757 ÷ 696   **16.** 1493 ÷ 152

Exercise No. 303
Addition of Fractions

Review the examples in Exercise No. 292 on page 108, No. 295 on page 109 and No. 299 on page 111. Also perform the following additions.

1. $\frac{3}{4} + \frac{7}{10}$ **4.** $\frac{1}{8} + \frac{2}{5}$ **7.** $\frac{1}{8} + \frac{1}{10}$ **10.** $\frac{1}{8} + \frac{9}{10}$
2. $\frac{3}{4} + \frac{9}{10}$ **5.** $\frac{1}{8} + \frac{3}{5}$ **8.** $\frac{1}{8} + \frac{3}{10}$
3. $\frac{1}{8} + \frac{1}{5}$ **6.** $\frac{1}{8} + \frac{4}{5}$ **9.** $\frac{1}{8} + \frac{7}{10}$

Exercise No. 304
Mental Multiplication

Multiply mentally the following.

1. 46 × 71   **8.** 46 × 78   **15.** 46 × 77
2. 56 × 72   **9.** 56 × 71   **16.** 56 × 78
3. 66 × 73   **10.** 66 × 72   **17.** 66 × 71
4. 76 × 74   **11.** 76 × 73   **18.** 76 × 72
5. 86 × 75   **12.** 86 × 74   **19.** 86 × 73
6. 96 × 76   **13.** 96 × 75   **20.** 96 × 74
7. 36 × 77   **14.** 36 × 76

Exercise No. 305
Subtraction of Fractions

Review the examples in Exercise No. 297 on page 110 and No. 301 on page 111. Also perform the following subtractions.

1. $1\frac{11}{24} - \frac{7}{8}$ **4.** $\frac{1}{2} - \frac{1}{5}$ **7.** $\frac{1}{2} - \frac{2}{5}$ **10.** $1\frac{3}{10} - \frac{2}{5}$
2. $1\frac{19}{24} - \frac{7}{8}$ **5.** $\frac{9}{10} - \frac{1}{5}$ **8.** $\frac{7}{10} - \frac{2}{5}$
3. $\frac{3}{10} - \frac{1}{5}$ **6.** $1\frac{1}{10} - \frac{1}{5}$ **9.** $1\frac{1}{10} - \frac{2}{5}$

Exercise No. 306
Mental Division
Divide mentally the following.

1. 5338 ÷ 772	**8.** 3606 ÷ 485	**15.** 5954 ÷ 666
2. 5393 ÷ 883	**9.** 4518 ÷ 596	**16.** 5887 ÷ 647
3. 6001 ÷ 994	**10.** 4711 ÷ 637	**17.** 7123 ÷ 758
4. 908 ÷ 145	**11.** 2284 ÷ 282	**18.** 8221 ÷ 869
5. 1576 ÷ 256	**12.** 3183 ÷ 393	**19.** 9257 ÷ 973
6. 1859 ÷ 263	**13.** 3956 ÷ 444	**20.** 1721 ÷ 184
7. 2736 ÷ 374	**14.** 4795 ÷ 555	

Exercise No. 307
Addition of Fractions
Review the examples in Exercise No. 295 on page 109, No. 297 on page 110 and No. 303 on page 112. Also perform the following additions.

1. $\frac{3}{8} + \frac{1}{5}$	**4.** $\frac{3}{8} + \frac{4}{5}$	**7.** $\frac{3}{8} + \frac{7}{10}$	**10.** $\frac{5}{8} + \frac{2}{5}$
2. $\frac{3}{8} + \frac{2}{5}$	**5.** $\frac{3}{8} + \frac{1}{10}$	**8.** $\frac{3}{8} + \frac{9}{10}$	
3. $\frac{3}{8} + \frac{3}{5}$	**6.** $\frac{3}{8} + \frac{3}{10}$	**9.** $\frac{5}{8} + \frac{1}{5}$	

Exercise No. 308
Mental Multiplication
Perform mentally the following multiplications.

1. 47 × 79	**8.** 47 × 87	**15.** 47 × 86
2. 57 × 81	**9.** 57 × 79	**16.** 57 × 87
3. 67 × 82	**10.** 67 × 81	**17.** 67 × 79
4. 77 × 83	**11.** 77 × 82	**18.** 77 × 81
5. 87 × 84	**12.** 87 × 83	**19.** 87 × 82
6. 97 × 85	**13.** 97 × 84	**20.** 97 × 83
7. 37 × 86	**14.** 37 × 85	

Exercise No. 309

Subtraction of Fractions

Review the examples in Exercise No. 301 on page 111 and No. 305 on page 112. Also perform the following subtractions.

1. $\frac{7}{10} - \frac{3}{5}$ 4. $1\frac{1}{2} - \frac{3}{5}$ 7. $1\frac{1}{2} - \frac{4}{5}$ 10. $\frac{9}{10} - \frac{1}{2}$

2. $\frac{9}{10} - \frac{3}{5}$ 5. $\frac{9}{10} - \frac{4}{5}$ 8. $1\frac{7}{10} - \frac{4}{5}$

3. $1\frac{3}{10} - \frac{3}{5}$ 6. $1\frac{1}{10} - \frac{4}{5}$ 9. $\frac{7}{10} - \frac{1}{2}$

Exercise No. 310

Mental Division

Divide mentally the following.

1. $5365 \div 748$ 8. $8304 \div 999$ 15. $6720 \div 679$

2. $6599 \div 851$ 9. $6075 \div 741$ 16. $7831 \div 784$

3. $7445 \div 962$ 10. $5241 \div 652$ 17. $8917 \div 895$

4. $1243 \div 173$ 11. $2682 \div 295$ 18. $9441 \div 946$

5. $2220 \div 284$ 12. $3411 \div 346$ 19. $1563 \div 157$

6. $6293 \div 777$ 13. $4471 \div 457$ 20. $2627 \div 268$

7. $7548 \div 888$ 14. $5667 \div 568$

Exercise No. 311

Addition of Fractions

Review the examples in Exercise No. 297 on page 110, No. 303 on page 112 and No. 307 on page 113. Also add the following.

1. $\frac{5}{8} + \frac{3}{5}$ 4. $\frac{5}{8} + \frac{3}{10}$ 7. $\frac{7}{8} + \frac{1}{5}$ 10. $\frac{7}{8} + \frac{4}{5}$

2. $\frac{5}{8} + \frac{4}{5}$ 5. $\frac{5}{8} + \frac{7}{10}$ 8. $\frac{7}{8} + \frac{2}{5}$

3. $\frac{5}{8} + \frac{1}{10}$ 6. $\frac{5}{8} + \frac{9}{10}$ 9. $\frac{7}{8} + \frac{3}{5}$

Exercise No. 312

Mental Multiplication

Multiply mentally the following.

1. 48×88 8. 48×96 15. 48×95

2. 58×89 9. 58×88 16. 58×96

3. 68×91 10. 68×89 17. 68×88

4. 78×92 11. 78×91 18. 78×89

5. 88×93 12. 88×92 19. 88×91

6. 98×94 13. 98×93 20. 98×92

7. 38×95 14. 38×94

Exercise No. 313
Subtraction of Fractions

Review the examples in Exercise No. 305 on page 112 and No. 309 on page 114. Also perform the following subtractions.

1. $1\frac{1}{10} - \frac{1}{2}$ 4. $\frac{4}{5} - \frac{1}{2}$ 7. $\frac{9}{20} - \frac{1}{4}$ 10. $1\frac{1}{20} - \frac{1}{4}$

2. $1\frac{3}{10} - \frac{1}{2}$ 5. $1\frac{1}{5} - \frac{1}{2}$ 8. $\frac{13}{20} - \frac{1}{4}$

3. $\frac{3}{5} - \frac{1}{2}$ 6. $1\frac{2}{5} - \frac{1}{2}$ 9. $\frac{17}{20} - \frac{1}{4}$

Exercise No. 314
Addition of Fractions

Review the examples in Exercise No. 303 on page 112, No. 307 on page 113 and No. 311 on page 114. Also perform the following additions.

1. $\frac{7}{8} + \frac{1}{10}$ 4. $\frac{7}{8} + \frac{9}{10}$ 7. $\frac{1}{3} + \frac{3}{5}$ 10. $\frac{1}{3} + \frac{3}{10}$

2. $\frac{7}{8} + \frac{3}{10}$ 5. $\frac{1}{3} + \frac{1}{5}$ 8. $\frac{1}{3} + \frac{4}{5}$

3. $\frac{7}{8} + \frac{7}{10}$ 6. $\frac{1}{3} + \frac{2}{5}$ 9. $\frac{1}{3} + \frac{1}{10}$

Exercise No. 315
Mental Multiplication

Multiply the following mentally.

1. 49×95 8. 49×97 15. 49×99

2. 59×96 9. 59×98 16. 59×95

3. 69×97 10. 69×99 17. 69×96

4. 79×98 11. 79×95 18. 79×97

5. 89×99 12. 89×96 19. 89×98

6. 99×95 13. 99×97 20. 99×99

7. 39×96 14. 39×98

Exercise No. 316
Subtraction of Fractions

Review the examples in Exercise No. 309 on page 114 and No. 313 on page 115. Also perform the following subtractions.

1. $\frac{7}{20} - \frac{1}{4}$ 4. $1\frac{3}{20} - \frac{1}{4}$ 7. $1\frac{7}{20} - \frac{3}{4}$ 10. $1\frac{1}{20} - \frac{3}{4}$
2. $\frac{11}{20} - \frac{1}{4}$ 5. $\frac{19}{20} - \frac{3}{4}$ 8. $1\frac{11}{20} - \frac{3}{4}$
3. $\frac{19}{20} - \frac{1}{4}$ 6. $1\frac{3}{20} - \frac{3}{4}$ 9. $\frac{17}{20} - \frac{3}{4}$

Exercise No. 317
Addition of Fractions

Review the examples in Exercise No. 307 on page 113, No. 311 on page 114 and No. 314 on page 115. Also perform the following additions.

1. $\frac{1}{3} + \frac{7}{10}$ 4. $\frac{2}{3} + \frac{2}{5}$ 7. $\frac{2}{3} + \frac{1}{10}$ 10. $\frac{2}{3} + \frac{9}{10}$
2. $\frac{1}{3} + \frac{9}{10}$ 5. $\frac{2}{3} + \frac{3}{5}$ 8. $\frac{2}{3} + \frac{3}{10}$
3. $\frac{2}{3} + \frac{1}{5}$ 6. $\frac{2}{3} + \frac{4}{5}$ 9. $\frac{2}{3} + \frac{7}{10}$

Exercise No. 318
Subtraction of Fractions

Review the examples in Exercise No. 313 on page 115 and No. 316 on this page. Also perform the following subtractions.

1. $1\frac{9}{20} - \frac{3}{4}$ 4. $\frac{21}{40} - \frac{1}{8}$ 7. $\frac{9}{40} - \frac{1}{8}$ 10. $1\frac{1}{40} - \frac{1}{8}$
2. $1\frac{13}{20} - \frac{3}{4}$ 5. $\frac{29}{40} - \frac{1}{8}$ 8. $\frac{17}{40} - \frac{1}{8}$
3. $\frac{13}{40} - \frac{1}{8}$ 6. $\frac{37}{40} - \frac{1}{8}$ 9. $\frac{33}{40} - \frac{1}{8}$

Exercise No. 319
Mental Division

Divide the following mentally.

1. $1066 \div 26$ 3. $1708 \div 28$ 5. $2511 \div 31$
2. $1377 \div 27$ 4. $2059 \div 29$ 6. $2912 \div 32$

7. 1023 ÷ 33   **12.** 2349 ÷ 29   **17.** 1586 ÷ 26
8. 1394 ÷ 34   **13.** 2821 ÷ 31   **18.** 1917 ÷ 27
9. 1326 ÷ 26   **14.** 992 ÷ 32   **19.** 2268 ÷ 28
10. 1647 ÷ 27   **15.** 1353 ÷ 33   **20.** 2639 ÷ 29
11. 1988 ÷ 28   **16.** 1734 ÷ 34

Exercise No. 320
Addition of Fractions
Review the examples in Exercise No. 311 on page 114, No. 314 on page 115 and No. 315 on page 115. Also perform the following additions.

1. $\frac{1}{6} + \frac{1}{5}$ **4.** $\frac{1}{6} + \frac{4}{5}$ **7.** $\frac{1}{6} + \frac{7}{10}$ **10.** $\frac{5}{6} + \frac{2}{5}$
2. $\frac{1}{6} + \frac{2}{5}$ **5.** $\frac{1}{6} + \frac{1}{10}$ **8.** $\frac{1}{6} + \frac{9}{10}$
3. $\frac{1}{6} + \frac{3}{5}$ **6.** $\frac{1}{6} + \frac{3}{10}$ **9.** $\frac{5}{6} + \frac{1}{5}$

Exercise No. 321
Subtraction of Fractions
Review the examples in Exercise No. 314 on page 115, No. 316 on page 116 and No. 320 above. Also perform the following subtractions.

1. $\frac{23}{40} - \frac{3}{8}$ **4.** $1\frac{7}{40} - \frac{3}{8}$ **7.** $1\frac{3}{40} - \frac{3}{8}$ **10.** $1\frac{1}{40} - \frac{5}{8}$
2. $\frac{31}{40} - \frac{3}{8}$ **5.** $\frac{19}{40} - \frac{3}{8}$ **8.** $1\frac{11}{40} - \frac{3}{8}$
3. $\frac{39}{40} - \frac{3}{8}$ **6.** $\frac{27}{40} - \frac{3}{8}$ **9.** $\frac{33}{40} - \frac{5}{8}$

Exercise No. 322
Mental Division
Divide the following mentally.

1. 1470 ÷ 35   **8.** 1806 ÷ 43   **15.** 1764 ÷ 42
2. 1872 ÷ 36   **9.** 1820 ÷ 35   **16.** 2236 ÷ 43
3. 2294 ÷ 37   **10.** 2232 ÷ 36   **17.** 2108 ÷ 34
4. 2736 ÷ 38   **11.** 2664 ÷ 37   **18.** 2520 ÷ 35
5. 3198 ÷ 39   **12.** 3116 ÷ 38   **19.** 2952 ÷ 36
6. 3772 ÷ 41   **13.** 3588 ÷ 39   **20.** 3404 ÷ 37
7. 1344 ÷ 42   **14.** 1312 ÷ 41

Exercise No. 323
Addition of Fractions

Review the examples in Exercise No. 314 on page 115, No. 317 on page 116 and No. 320 on page 117. Also perform the following additions.

1. $\frac{5}{6} + \frac{3}{5}$ 3. $\frac{5}{6} + \frac{1}{10}$ 5. $\frac{5}{6} + \frac{7}{10}$

2. $\frac{5}{6} + \frac{4}{5}$ 4. $\frac{5}{6} + \frac{3}{10}$ 6. $\frac{5}{6} + \frac{9}{10}$

Exercise No. 324
Subtraction of Fractions

Review the examples in Exercise No. 318 on page 116 and No. 321 on page 117. Also perform the following subtractions.

1. $1\frac{9}{40} - \frac{5}{8}$ 4. $\frac{37}{40} - \frac{5}{8}$ 7. $1\frac{3}{40} - \frac{7}{8}$ 10. $1\frac{27}{40} - \frac{7}{8}$

2. $1\frac{17}{40} - \frac{5}{8}$ 5. $1\frac{11}{40} - \frac{5}{8}$ 8. $1\frac{11}{40} - \frac{7}{8}$

3. $\frac{29}{40} - \frac{5}{8}$ 6. $1\frac{21}{40} - \frac{5}{8}$ 9. $1\frac{19}{40} - \frac{7}{8}$

Exercise No. 325
Mental Division

Divide the following mentally.

1. 1892 ÷ 44   8. 2236 ÷ 52   15. 2193 ÷ 51
2. 2385 ÷ 45   9. 2332 ÷ 44   16. 2756 ÷ 52
3. 2898 ÷ 46   10. 2835 ÷ 45   17. 2772 ÷ 44
4. 3431 ÷ 47   11. 3358 ÷ 46   18. 3285 ÷ 45
5. 3984 ÷ 48   12. 3901 ÷ 47   19. 3818 ÷ 46
6. 4557 ÷ 49   13. 4464 ÷ 48   20. 4371 ÷ 47
7. 1683 ÷ 51   14. 1617 ÷ 49

Exercise No. 326
Addition of Fractions

Review the examples in Exercise No. 317 on page 116, No. 320 on page 117 and No. 323 on this page.

Exercise No. 327
Subtraction of Fractions

Review the examples in Exercise No. 321 on page 117 and No. 324 on page 118. Also perform the following subtractions.

1. $\frac{39}{40} - \frac{7}{8}$
2. $1\frac{7}{40} - \frac{7}{8}$
3. $1\frac{23}{40} - \frac{7}{8}$

4. $1\frac{31}{40} - \frac{7}{8}$
5. $\frac{8}{15} - \frac{1}{3}$
6. $\frac{11}{15} - \frac{1}{3}$

7. $\frac{14}{15} - \frac{1}{3}$
8. $1\frac{2}{15} - \frac{1}{3}$
9. $\frac{13}{30} - \frac{1}{3}$

10. $\frac{19}{30} - \frac{1}{3}$

Exercise No. 328
Mental Division

Divide the following mentally.

1. $2332 \div 53$
2. $2916 \div 54$
3. $3520 \div 55$
4. $4144 \div 56$
5. $4788 \div 57$
6. $5452 \div 58$
7. $2006 \div 59$

8. $2684 \div 61$
9. $2862 \div 53$
10. $3456 \div 54$
11. $4070 \div 55$
12. $4704 \div 56$
13. $5358 \div 57$
14. $1972 \div 58$

15. $2596 \div 59$
16. $3294 \div 61$
17. $3392 \div 53$
18. $3996 \div 54$
19. $4620 \div 55$
20. $5264 \div 56$

Exercise No. 329
Addition of Fractions

Review the examples in Exercise No. 320 on page 117 and 323 on page 118.

Exercise No. 330
Subtraction of Fractions

Review the examples in Exercise No. 321 on page 117 and No. 324 on page 118. Also perform the following subtractions.

1. $1\frac{1}{30} - \frac{1}{3}$
2. $1\frac{7}{30} - \frac{1}{3}$
3. $\frac{13}{15} - \frac{2}{3}$

4. $1\frac{1}{15} - \frac{2}{3}$
5. $1\frac{4}{15} - \frac{2}{3}$
6. $1\frac{7}{15} - \frac{2}{3}$

7. $\frac{23}{30} - \frac{2}{3}$
8. $\frac{29}{30} - \frac{2}{3}$
9. $1\frac{11}{30} - \frac{2}{3}$

10. $1\frac{17}{30} - \frac{2}{3}$

Exercise No. 331
Mental Division
Divide the following mentally.

1. $2790 \div 62$
2. $3465 \div 63$
3. $4160 \div 64$
4. $4875 \div 65$
5. $5610 \div 66$
6. $6365 \div 67$
7. $2380 \div 68$

8. $3105 \div 69$
9. $3410 \div 62$
10. $4095 \div 63$
11. $4800 \div 64$
12. $5525 \div 65$
13. $6270 \div 66$
14. $2345 \div 67$

15. $3060 \div 68$
16. $3795 \div 69$
17. $4030 \div 62$
18. $4725 \div 63$
19. $5440 \div 64$
20. $6175 \div 65$

Exercise No. 332
Mental Division
Divide the following mentally.

1. $3266 \div 71$
2. $4032 \div 72$
3. $4818 \div 73$
4. $5624 \div 74$
5. $6450 \div 75$
6. $7296 \div 76$
7. $2772 \div 77$

8. $3588 \div 78$
9. $3976 \div 71$
10. $4752 \div 72$
11. $5548 \div 73$
12. $6364 \div 74$
13. $7200 \div 75$
14. $2736 \div 76$

15. $3542 \div 77$
16. $4368 \div 78$
17. $4686 \div 71$
18. $5472 \div 72$
19. $6278 \div 73$
20. $7104 \div 74$

Exercise No. 333
Subtraction of Fractions
Review the examples in Exercise No. 324 on page 118 and No. 330 on page 119. Also perform the following subtractions.

1. $\frac{11}{30} - \frac{1}{6}$
2. $\frac{17}{30} - \frac{1}{6}$
3. $\frac{23}{30} - \frac{1}{6}$

4. $\frac{29}{30} - \frac{1}{6}$
5. $\frac{4}{15} - \frac{1}{6}$
6. $\frac{7}{15} - \frac{1}{6}$

7. $\frac{13}{15} - \frac{1}{6}$
8. $1\frac{1}{15} - \frac{1}{6}$
9. $1\frac{1}{30} - \frac{5}{6}$

10. $1\frac{7}{30} - \frac{5}{8}$

Exercise No. 334
Mental Division
Divide the following mentally.

1. $3713 \div 79$
2. $4617 \div 81$
3. $5494 \div 82$

4. $6391 \div 83$
5. $7308 \div 84$
6. $8245 \div 85$

7. $3182 \div 86$
8. $4089 \div 87$
9. $4503 \div 79$

10. 5427 ÷ 81   14. 3145 ÷ 85   18. 6237 ÷ 81
11. 6314 ÷ 82   15. 4042 ÷ 86   19. 7134 ÷ 82
12. 7221 ÷ 83   16. 4959 ÷ 87   20. 8051 ÷ 83
13. 8148 ÷ 84   17. 5293 ÷ 79

Exercise No. 335
Subtraction of Fractions
Review the examples in Exercise No. 330 on page 119
and No. 333 on page 120. Also perform the following
subtractions.

1. $1\frac{13}{30} - \frac{5}{6}$ 3. $\frac{14}{15} - \frac{5}{6}$ 5. $1\frac{8}{15} - \frac{5}{6}$
2. $1\frac{19}{30} - \frac{5}{6}$ 4. $1\frac{2}{15} - \frac{5}{6}$ 6. $1\frac{11}{15} - \frac{5}{6}$

Exercise No. 336
Mental Division
Divide the following mentally.

1. 4224 ÷ 88   8. 4608 ÷ 96   15. 4560 ÷ 95
2. 5162 ÷ 89   9. 5104 ÷ 88   16. 5568 ÷ 96
3. 6188 ÷ 91   10. 6052 ÷ 89   17. 5984 ÷ 88
4. 7176 ÷ 92   11. 7098 ÷ 91   18. 6942 ÷ 89
5. 8184 ÷ 93   12. 8096 ÷ 92   19. 8008 ÷ 91
6. 9212 ÷ 94   13. 9114 ÷ 93   20. 9016 ÷ 92
7. 3610 ÷ 95   14. 3572 ÷ 94

Exercise No. 337
Mental Division
Divide the following mentally.

1. 4655 ÷ 95   8. 4753 ÷ 97   15. 4851 ÷ 99
2. 5664 ÷ 96   9. 5782 ÷ 98   16. 5605 ÷ 95
3. 6693 ÷ 97   10. 6831 ÷ 99   17. 6624 ÷ 96
4. 7742 ÷ 98   11. 7505 ÷ 95   18. 7663 ÷ 97
5. 8811 ÷ 99   12. 8544 ÷ 96   19. 8722 ÷ 98
6. 9405 ÷ 95   13. 9603 ÷ 97   20. 9801 ÷ 99
7. 3744 ÷ 96   14. 3822 ÷ 98

DECIMALS IN GENERAL

For the purposes of this book our interest in decimals centers in the equivalence of value between certain decimals and common fractions. Decimal parts of a number that may be represented as simple fractions of that number are known as *aliquot parts* of it. Thus, $12\frac{1}{2}$, 25 and $33\frac{1}{3}$ are aliquot parts of 100, being respectively equal to $\frac{1}{8}$, $\frac{1}{4}$ and $\frac{1}{3}$ of 100.

A knowledge of aliquot parts simplifies many arithmetical calculations. Thus if it be required to multiply 7928 by 25, the simplest way is to annex two 0's to 7928, making it 792800, and then divide by 4, since 25 is $\frac{1}{4}$ of 100. The answer, which may easily be figured mentally, comes to 198200.

Again, if we wanted to know the cost of 25 gross of penholders at $66\frac{2}{3}$¢ per dozen, we would figure that 1 gross costs $\$\frac{2}{3} \times 12$, or \$8, and that 25 gross therefore cost \$200.

Everybody with any degree of arithmetical training or experience is familiar with the equivalent decimal values for halves, quarters, eighths, thirds, sixths, fifths, tenths, twentieths, twenty-fifths and fiftieths. It is not difficult to extend the list of memorized values so as to include sixteenths and twelfths, and with this knowledge to make rapid calculations of values in thirty-seconds and twenty-fourths.

The succeeding exercises in decimals are designed toward this end. The student is drilled in representing the values of various fractions as decimals of an increasingly higher number of

places. No tables are given because values are more quickly learned by repeated calculation than by any effort at mere memorization.

Exercise No. 338
Two-Place Decimal Values
Express the following fractions as decimals of two places. Use fractional terminations where necessary. Thus, $\frac{1}{3}$ expressed as a two-place decimal becomes $.33\frac{1}{3}$.

1. $\frac{1}{8}$ 4. $\frac{7}{8}$ 7. $\frac{1}{6}$ 10. $\frac{2}{5}$
2. $\frac{3}{8}$ 5. $\frac{1}{3}$ 8. $\frac{5}{6}$ 11. $\frac{3}{5}$
3. $\frac{5}{8}$ 6. $\frac{2}{3}$ 9. $\frac{1}{5}$ 12. $\frac{4}{5}$

Repeat this exercise three times.

Exercise No. 339
Multiplying Three Figures by Two
Multiply mentally the following.

No new principles are involved in multiplications of this type. The student is simply asked to apply the methods which he has already learned to larger numbers.

1. 111×26 4. 442×29 7. 721×33 10. 152×27
2. 222×27 5. 551×31 8. 832×34
3. 331×28 6. 612×32 9. 941×26

Exercise No. 340
Two-Place Decimal Values
Review the examples in Exercise No. 338 above.
Express the following as decimals of two places.

1. $\frac{1}{16}$ 5. $\frac{9}{16}$ 9. $\frac{1}{12}$ 13. $\frac{1}{32}$
2. $\frac{3}{16}$ 6. $\frac{11}{16}$ 10. $\frac{5}{12}$ 14. $\frac{1}{24}$
3. $\frac{5}{16}$ 7. $\frac{13}{16}$ 11. $\frac{7}{12}$
4. $\frac{7}{16}$ 8. $\frac{15}{16}$ 12. $\frac{11}{12}$

Repeat this exercise three times.

Exercise No. 341
Multiplying Three Figures by Two
Multiply mentally the following.

1. 121 × 35
2. 232 × 36
3. 343 × 37
4. 451 × 38
5. 562 × 39
6. 623 × 41
7. 731 × 42
8. 842 × 43
9. 953 × 35
10. 161 × 36

SHORT CUTS

There are a number of devices for shortening the work of calculation in specific cases, though most of the methods usually included under this head have only a limited practical value because they are applicable only in highly special cases. A few methods, like horizontal addition and combined addition and subtraction have first-class utility. A variety of short cuts of varying degrees of value are given in the following pages without any attempt to classify them. The student should become familiar with all of them because there is always benefit in viewing numbers from as many angles as possible.

Exercise No. 342
Horizontal Addition

The term *horizontal addition* is applied to the adding of numbers that are not arranged in column form. There is often an unnecessary waste of time in arranging numbers in the form of columns. This is particularly true when the numbers to be added are on bills, invoices, etc. Values on such papers may be totalled by writing down each partial sum as it is arrived at, and then making a final addition.

Consider the first of the following examples. The sum of the units is 37, the sum of the tens is 45, etc. The sums of the various orders are successively set down in the form shown below, and then added.

$$
\begin{array}{r}
37 \\
45 \\
14 \\
\underline{16} \\
17887
\end{array}
$$

The process might of course be shortened somewhat by adding two orders at a time.

Add the following.

1. $32 + $183 + $54 + $3486 + $569 + $9375 + $85 + $4103
2. $875 + $284 + $37 + $5200 + $398 + $62 + $74 + $2168 + $720
3. 763 + 827 + 49 + 5283 + 768 + 2175
4. 1536 + 8973 + 5178 + 926 + 8259 + 36 + 867
5. 9365 + 8375 + 1473 + 826 + 4123 + 15378
6. 986 + 325 + 7261 + 5820 + 569 + 8371
7. 6275 + 5183 + 985 + 3267 + 75 + 1528
8. 1738 + 9168 + 8273 + 5298 + 9 + 6832 + 65
9. $783.52 + $41.27 + $837.45 + $9681.73 + $48.26 + $912.78 + $91.75 + $683.12 + $41.83 + $591.87 + $291.83 + $758.32 + $58.67
10. 46235 + 8976 + 5807 + 98397 + 68325 + 892 + 5140 + 6839 + 326 + 2125

Exercise No. 343

Multiplying Three Figures by Two

Multiply mentally the following.

1. 131×44	4. 464×47	7. 743×51	10. 172×45
2. 242×45	5. 571×48	8. 854×52	
3. 353×46	6. 632×49	9. 961×44	

Exercise No. 344

Four-Place Decimal Values

Review the examples in Exercises No. 338 and 340 on page 123.

Express the fractions listed in Exercise No. 340 as decimals of four places. This is done by simply writing the value as parts of 100 of the terminal fractions of the proper two-place decimals. Thus, $\frac{1}{16}$, which is .06$\frac{1}{4}$ as a two-place decimal, becomes .0625 as a decimal of four places. Again, $\frac{1}{12}$ is .08$\frac{1}{3}$ or .0833$\frac{1}{3}$.

Exercise No. 345
Multiplying Three Figures by Two
Multiply mentally the following.

1. 141 × 53	**4.** 474 × 56	**7.** 752 × 59	**10.** 185 × 54
2. 252 × 54	**5.** 585 × 57	**8.** 863 × 61	
3. 363 × 55	**6.** 641 × 58	**9.** 974 × 53	

Exercise No. 346
Combined Addition and Subtraction

It sometimes becomes necessary to subtract the sum of several numbers from a single number. If the numbers to be added are arranged in column form, this may be done at what amounts to one operation by a very simple process.

The numbers may be arranged either as a sum with a missing addend, as in the examples given for practice, or else with the minuend written at the top with underscoring and the difference written at the bottom, as in the examples shown for illustration.

The so-called carry method of subtraction is used. The sum of each successive column is subtracted from the corresponding figure of the minuend plus as many tens as may be necessary to make the subtraction possible. The number of tens thus used is then added to the next column.

To illustrate: from 122808 take the sum of 35635, and 68921.

$$122808$$

$$35635$$
$$68921$$

$$18252$$

The sum of 5 and 1 is subtracted from 8; write 2 and carry 0. Subtract 5 from 10; write 5 and carry 1 because 1 ten was used to make the subtraction possible. With

1 to carry, the next column adds to 16; subtract this from 18 and again carry 1. The next column adds to 14; subtract this from 22 and carry 2 because 2 tens were needed to make the subtraction possible in this case. Carrying 2 and subtracting from 12 gives the final necessary figure, 1.

The method of carrying may be made still more clear by taking an example that involves larger numbers; from 3744 subtract the sum of 366, 466, 566, 666, 766, 266 and 466.

$$
\begin{array}{r}
3744 \\
\hline
366 \\
466 \\
566 \\
666 \\
766 \\
266 \\
466 \\
\hline
182
\end{array}
$$

The sum of the first column, 42, is subtracted from 44 because 44 is the next higher number ending in 4 from which a subtraction can be made; 4 is carried. The sum of the second column, 46, is subtracted from 54 because 54 is the next higher number ending in 4 from which a subtraction can be made; 5 is carried. The sum of the hundreds' column subtracted from 39 leaves 1.

In the following examples fill in in each case the missing number that will make all the numbers add to the total shown.

1.	$24.96	2.	6016	3.	$29.44	4.	6144
	6.24		376		7.36		384
	1.56		141		1.84		24576
	12.48		188		3.68		3072
	.98		1504		58.88		145
	3.12		752		1.38		49152
	(?)		(?)		(?)		(?)
	$149.18		105233		$220.34		181777

5.	6.	7.	8.
864	$168.86	$475.17	$286.09
108	10.56	46.82	5304.62
81	1.32	120.08	20463.20
5296	.96	2461.50	607.05
3456	2.64	500.07	6315.46
432	84.48	1208.92	73.90
(?)	(?)	(?)	(?)
11965	$944.66	$12933.16	$63452.87

Exercise No. 347

Multiplying Three Figures by Two

Multiply mentally the following.

1. 151×62 **4.** 484×65 **7.** 761×68 **10.** 194×63

2. 262×63 **5.** 595×66 **8.** 872×69

3. 373×64 **6.** 656×67 **9.** 983×62

Exercise No. 348

Five-Place Decimal Values

Review the examples in Exercises No. 338 and 340 on page 123 and No. 344 on page 126.

Express the following fractions as decimals of five places.

To find values in thirty-seconds, add $.0312\frac{1}{2}$ to the next lower value in sixteenths, etc. The calculation is clearer in the mind if both sixteenths and thirty-seconds are first thought of as decimals of four places. Changing the four-place answer to five places is the work of an instant.

To find values in twenty-fourths, add $.0416\frac{2}{3}$ to the next lower value in twelfths, etc. In writing answers, drop final $\frac{1}{3}$, and raise final $\frac{2}{3}$ to make the last figure a 7.

1. $\frac{1}{32}$ **4.** $\frac{7}{32}$ **7.** $\frac{13}{32}$ **10.** $\frac{19}{32}$ **13.** $\frac{25}{32}$

2. $\frac{3}{32}$ **5.** $\frac{9}{32}$ **8.** $\frac{15}{32}$ **11.** $\frac{21}{32}$ **14.** $\frac{27}{32}$

3. $\frac{5}{32}$ **6.** $\frac{11}{32}$ **9.** $\frac{17}{32}$ **12.** $\frac{23}{32}$ **15.** $\frac{29}{32}$

16. $\frac{31}{32}$ 18. $\frac{5}{24}$ 20. $\frac{11}{24}$ 22. $\frac{17}{24}$ 24. $\frac{23}{24}$

17. $\frac{1}{24}$ 19. $\frac{7}{24}$ 21. $\frac{13}{24}$ 23. $\frac{19}{24}$

Exercise No. 349

Multiplying Three Figures by Two

Multiply mentally the following.

1. 141 × 71   **4.** 474 × 74   **7.** 747 × 77   **10.** 173 × 72
2. 252 × 72   **5.** 585 × 75   **8.** 851 × 78
3. 363 × 73   **6.** 696 × 76   **9.** 962 × 71

Exercise No. 350

Multiplying by a Near Number

It sometimes happens that a multiplier is a little more or a little less than 100, 1000, 10000, etc. In cases of this kind it is quickest to multiply by the round number and then add or subtract the necessary difference. For example, multiply $385.20 by 998. We multiply the dollar value by 1000 and subtract from this product twice $385.20, thus:

$$\begin{array}{r} \$385200 \\ 770.40 \\ \hline \$384429.60 \end{array}$$

Multiply the following. The student should be able to do most of these mentally.

1. $425 × 999   **4.** $258.30 × 104   **7.** $989 × 992
2. $865 × 98   **5.** $827.58 × 1003   **8.** $99 × 97
3. $735.25 × 998   **6.** $516 × 1.02   **9.** $1005 × 1002

Exercise No. 351

Multiplying Three Figures by Two

Multiply mentally the following.

1. 131 × 79 **4.** 464 × 83 **7.** 797 × 86 **10.** 152 × 81
2. 242 × 81 **5.** 575 × 84 **8.** 838 × 87
3. 353 × 82 **6.** 686 × 85 **9.** 941 × 79

Exercise No. 352
Review of Decimals
Review the examples in Exercise No. 340 on page 123, No. 344 on page 126 and No. 348 on page 129.

Exercise No. 353
Multiplying Three Figures by Two
Multiply mentally the following.

1. 141 × 88 **4.** 474 × 92 **7.** 747 × 95 **10.** 171 × 89
2. 252 × 89 **5.** 585 × 93 **8.** 858 × 96
3. 363 × 91 **6.** 696 × 94 **9.** 969 × 88

Exercise No. 354
Aliquot Parts in Multiplication
Reference has already been made to the fact that multiplication may be simplified by considering one of the factors as an aliquot part of some number ending in two or more 0's. Thus, 628 × 25 would be solved by multiplying 628 by 100 and dividing by 4; the answer comes to 15700. Again, multiplying 56 × 75 would be done most quickly by taking $\frac{3}{4}$ of 56 and then multiplying by 100.

Perform the following multiplications by the method of aliquot parts.

1. $35 × 15 **6.** $36 × 25 **11.** $35 × 18
2. $42 × 18 **7.** $52 × 250 **12.** $28 × 450
3. $24 × 16 **8.** $42 × 350 **13.** $36 × 33⅓
4. $18 × 45 **9.** $150 × 48 **14.** $72 × 16⅔
5. $72 × 75 **10.** $64 × 25 **15.** $96 × 12½

Exercise No. 355
Multiplying Three Figures by Two
Multiply mentally the following. Do not use short cuts.

1. 152×95 **4.** 485×98 **7.** 758×96 **10.** 194×99
2. 263×96 **5.** 596×99 **8.** 869×97
3. 374×97 **6.** 647×95 **9.** 973×98

Exercise No. 356
Review of Decimals
Review the examples in Exercise No. 344 on page 126 and No. 348 on page 129.

Exercise No. 357
Multiplying Three Figures by Three
Multiply mentally the following. Add together the first two partial products before determining the third.

1. 111×101 **5.** 551×141 **9.** 941×181
2. 222×111 **6.** 612×151 **10.** 152×191
3. 331×121 **7.** 721×161
4. 442×131 **8.** 832×171

Exercise No. 358
Simplifying the Multiplier
Sometimes a multiplier is of such a nature that one part of it may be taken as an exact multiple of another. In such cases an operation is eliminated by making a single multiplication of the first-found partial product instead of two multiplications of the original multiplicand. In the example at the left above, the 18 in the multiplier is equal to 3 times the 6. We therefore multiply the first partial product by 3 instead of multiplying the original multiplicand by 18. In the example at the right, 56 being equal

to 8 times 7, we multiply first by 8, placing the result in the proper position, and then multiply this partial product by 7.

2574	5462
186	856
15444	43696
46332	305872
478764	4675472

Multiply the following by this method.

1. $385.85 × 642
2. $742.50 × 328
3. $82615 × 729
4. $4265.25 × 255

5. $9541.12 × 546
6. $172.48 × 763
7. $2153.28 × 18624
8. $530.75 × 16412

Exercise No. 359
Multiplying Three Figures by Three
Multiply mentally the following.

1. 121 × 202
2. 232 × 212
3. 343 × 222
4. 451 × 232

5. 562 × 242
6. 623 × 252
7. 731 × 262
8. 842 × 272

9. 953 × 282
10. 161 × 292

Exercise No. 360
Review of Decimals
Review the examples in Exercise No. 348 on page 129.

Exercise No. 361
Multiplying Three Figures by Three
Multiply mentally the following.

1. 131 × 303
2. 242 × 313
3. 353 × 323
4. 464 × 333

5. 571 × 343
6. 632 × 353
7. 743 × 363
8. 854 × 373

9. 961 × 383
10. 172 × 393

Exercise No. 362
Multiplication by Factoring

When a multiplier can be taken as the product of two factors, it may be quicker to make separate multiplications by each of these factors than to proceed in the ordinary manner. Take the example 632 × 156. In the illustrations below, the one at the left shows the ordinary method. At the right the multiplier is split up into the factors 13 and 12; the multiplicand is multiplied by 13 and the result is then multiplied by 12.

$$
\begin{array}{cc}
632 & 632 \\
156 & 13 \\
\hline
3792 & 8216 \\
3160 & 12 \\
632 & \hline \\
\hline
98592 & 98592
\end{array}
$$

Multiply the following by this method.

1. 759 × 182	**4.** 656 × 285	**7.** 542 × 221
2. 684 × 169	**5.** 309 × 289	**8.** 327 × 224
3. 327 × 228	**6.** 728 × 324	**9.** 986 × 196

Exercise No. 363
Multiplying Three Figures by Three

Multiply mentally the following.

1. 141 × 404	**5.** 585 × 444	**9.** 974 × 484
2. 252 × 414	**6.** 641 × 454	**10.** 185 × 494
3. 363 × 424	**7.** 752 × 464	
4. 474 × 434	**8.** 863 × 474	

Exercise No. 364
Factors Between 11 and 19

A quick way to calculate the product of two numbers between 11 and 19 is to add the units of one number to the whole of the other, annex 0 and add the product of the units of both numbers. Thus, to multiply 16 × 18:

16 and 8 are 24; call this 240 and add 48, making 288. The same result would be reached by adding 6 to 18. Multiply by this method:

1. 14 × 15
2. 18 × 19
3. 15 × 17

4. 15 × 16
5. 13 × 15
6. 13 × 19

7. 16 × 17
8. 14 × 16
9. 19 × 19

Exercise No. 365
Multiplying Three Figures by Three
Multiply mentally the following.

1. 151 × 505
2. 262 × 515
3. 373 × 525
4. 484 × 535

5. 595 × 545
6. 656 × 555
7. 761 × 565
8. 872 × 575

9. 983 × 585
10. 194 × 595

Exercise No. 366
Multiplying by 11
When the multiplicand consists of two figures the sum of which is less than 10, the product is found by writing the two figures of the multiplicand with their sum between them. Thus, to multiply 62 by 11 we write 6 and 2 with the sum of 6 and 2 between these figures, obtaining 682.

To multiply larger numbers by 11, apply the following rule. Beginning at the right, write the units' figure of the multiplicand, then successively the units plus the tens, the tens plus the hundreds, the hundreds plus the thousands, etc., carrying wherever necessary, and ending with the highest order of the multiplicand, or the highest order plus the carrying figure. Thus, to multiply 4762 by 11: write 2; add 2 and 6 and write 8; add 6 and 7, write 3 and carry 1; add 7 and 4, increase it by the 1 carried, write 2 and carry 1; add this 1 to 4 and write 5. Answer, 52382.

Multiply the following by this method.

1. $5136 × 11   5. $41268.45 × 11
2. $72638 × 11   6. $3275.75 × 11
3. $514832 × 11   7. $48263.25 × 11
4. $37281.05 × 11   8. $94873.30 × 11

Exercise No. 367

Multiplying Three Figures by Three
Multiply mentally the following.

1. 141 × 606   5. 585 × 646   9. 962 × 686
2. 252 × 616   6. 696 × 656   10. 173 × 696
3. 363 × 626   7. 747 × 666
4. 474 × 636   8. 851 × 676

Exercise No. 368

Multiplying by 21, 31, 41, etc.
Setting down the product from right to left, write the units' figure of the multiplicand, then multiply each order of the multiplicand by the tens' figure of the multiplier, increasing the result in each case by the next higher order of the multiplicand and any necessary carrying figure.

Example, multiply 387 by 41; write 7; multiply 7 by 4, add the 8 of the multiplicand, making 36, write 6 and carry 3; multiply 8 by 4, add the 3 of the multiplicand and the carried 3, making 38, write 8 and carry 3; multiply 3 by 4 and add the carried 3 making 15, write 15. Answer, 15867.

Multiply by this method:

1. $2735.50 × 51   5. $7415.40 × 61
2. $1824.75 × 81   6. $8291.25 × 91
3. $5104.30 × 31   7. $2134.15 × 71
4. $6238.65 × 21   8. $5827.80 × 41

Exercise No. 369
Multiplying Three Figures by Three

Multiply mentally the following.

1. 131 × 707	**5.** 575 × 747	**9.** 941 × 787
2. 242 × 717	**6.** 686 × 757	**10.** 152 × 797
3. 353 × 727	**7.** 797 × 767	
4. 464 × 737	**8.** 838 × 777	

Exercise No. 370
Squares of Numbers

The square of a number is the number multiplied by itself. Squares may be determined quickly if the given number is considered to be the sum of two numbers. In algebra such a sum would ordinarily be taken as $a + b$ and its square would be $a^2 + 2\,ab + b^2$. In regular arithmetical cases a becomes the tens of the number and b the units. Thus, 25 is 20 + 5, and 146 is 140 + 6. The algebraic formula for the square of the sum of two numbers is expressed as the square of the first plus twice the product of the first by the second plus the square of the second. Thus, 25 squared is 20 × 20 (400) plus 2 × 20 × 5 (200) plus 5 × 5 (25); the total is 625.

In computing squares by this principle you may immediately annex the square of the second to the square of the first, and then add twice the product of the first by the second. Thus in squaring 25 you would immediately say 425, and then add to this 2 × 20 × 5 (200), making 625. In squaring 146 you immediately say 19636 and add to this 2 × 140 × 6 (1680), making 21316. Always allow two places for the square of the second. Thus in squaring 61 the first partial product is 3601, to which 120 is added to make 3721.

In squaring numbers on paper the following method will be found rapid where large numbers are involved. Set the given number down twice as if for regular multiplication. Assuming that it is considered to consist of tens and units,

multiply units by units, write units in the result and carry the tens. Add the two given tens together, multiply this sum by the given units, add the carried figure, write tens in the result and carry hundreds. Multiply tens by tens, add the carried figure and write the result.

67	134	1613
67	134	1613
4489	17956	2601769

In the first illustrative example at the left, $7 \times 7 = 49$, write 9 and carry 4; $6 + 6 = 12$, $12 \times 7 = 84$, $84 + 4 = 88$, write 8 and carry 8; $6 \times 6 = 36$, $36 + 8 = 44$.

In the second example, $4 \times 4 = 16$, write 6 and carry 1; $13 + 13 = 26$, $26 \times 4 = 104$, $104 + 1 = 105$, write 5 and carry 10; $13 \times 13 = 169$, $169 + 10 = 179$, write 179.

The third example is worked somewhat differently because here the parts of the number are considered to be 1600 and 13. $13 \times 13 = 169$, write 69 (two figures) and carry 1; $16 + 16 = 32$, $32 \times 13 = 416$, $416 + 1 = 417$, write 17 and carry 4; $16 \times 16 = 256$, $256 + 4 = 260$, write 260.

Find the squares of the following numbers. Do all the examples first by the first method, then by the second method.

1. 74	**4.** 64	**7.** 124	**10.** 197	**13.** 1314
2. 93	**5.** 38	**8.** 146	**11.** 1112	**14.** 1516
3. 82	**6.** 112	**9.** 168	**12.** 1213	**15.** 1719

Exercise No. 371
Multiplying Three Figures by Three
Multiply mentally the following.

1. 141×808	**5.** 585×848	**9.** 969×888
2. 252×818	**6.** 696×858	**10.** 171×898
3. 363×828	**7.** 747×868	
4. 474×838	**8.** 858×878	

Exercise No. 372
Multiplying When Units Are Alike
The following method is a variation of that explained in connection with the squaring of numbers.

```
  47        613
  67        913
————      ——————
3149      559669
```

In the illustration at the left, 7 × 7 = 49, write 9 and carry 4; 6 + 4 = 10, 10 × 7 = 70, 70 + 4 = 74, write 4 and carry 7; 4 × 6 = 24, 24 + 7 = 31, write 31.

In the illustration at the right, 13 × 13 = 169, write 69 and carry 1; 6 + 9 = 15, 15 × 13 = 195, 195 + 1 = 196, write 96 and carry 1; 6 × 9 = 54, 54 + 1 = 55, write 55.

Perform the following multiplications by this method.

1. 136 × 56
2. 159 × 79
3. 172 × 92
4. 195 × 115
5. 234 × 174
6. 217 × 197
7. 516 × 816
8. 714 × 314
9. 217 × 917

Exercise No. 373
Multiplying Three Figures by Three

1. 152 × 909
2. 263 × 919
3. 374 × 929
4. 485 × 939
5. 596 × 949
6. 647 × 959
7. 758 × 969
8. 869 × 979
9. 973 × 989
10. 184 × 999

Exercise No. 374
Multiplying When Tens or Hundreds Are Alike
This is a variation of the method explained in Exercise No. 372 above.

```
  83        717
  89        714
————      ——————
7387      511938
```

In the example on page 139, $3 \times 9 = 27$, write 7 and carry 2; $3 + 9 = 12$, $12 \times 8 = 96$, $96 + 2 = 98$, write 8 and carry 9; $8 \times 8 = 64$, $64 + 9 = 73$, write 73.

In the example on page 139, $17 \times 14 = 238$, write 38 and carry 2; $17 + 14 = 31$, $31 \times 7 = 217$, $217 + 2 = 219$, write 19 and carry 2; $7 \times 7 = 49$, $49 + 2 = 51$, write 51.

Multiply the following by this method.

1. 92×93	**4.** 92×97	**7.** 416×418
2. 62×65	**5.** 213×215	**8.** 509×519
3. 84×87	**6.** 321×312	**9.** 913×917

Exercise No. 375

Square of Numbers Ending in 5

If a number to be squared consists of tens and units, and if the units are 5, then twice the product of the first part by the second is equal to the given number of tens. Thus, in 25×25, $20 \times 5 \times 2$ is equal to 20×10; in 35×35, $30 \times 5 \times 2$ is equal to 30×10. Accordingly when dealing with numbers of this type we may at once annex 25 to the product of the given tens multiplied by one more than the given tens. That is to say, $25 \times 25 = 625$, in which the 6 represents 3×2; $35 \times 35 = 1225$ in which the 12 represents 4×3; $45 \times 45 = 2025$, in which the 20 represents 5×4, etc.

Find the squares of the following numbers by this method.

1. 45	**4.** 75	**7.** 115	**10.** 175	**13.** 335
2. 55	**5.** 85	**8.** 135	**11.** 195	**14.** 355
3. 65	**6.** 95	**9.** 155	**12.** 315	**15.** 375

Exercise No. 376

Multiplying Like Tens with Units Making 10

The principle explained above applies to any case in which the tens are alike and the sum of the units is 10.

Thus the product of 46×44 is 2024. We arrive at this by multiplying 4×5, making 20, and writing after this the product of 4×6 or 24.

Multiply in this manner the following.

1. 23×27	**4.** 103×107	**7.** 178×172
2. 41×49	**5.** 112×118	**8.** 169×161
3. 36×34	**6.** 154×156	**9.** 192×198

Exercise No. 377

Squaring Numbers Ending in 25

When a number ends in 25, like 725 for instance, we may take it as the sum of two numbers of which one represents hundreds and the other tens and units. In such cases twice the product of the first part by the second is equal to 50 times the first part. The result of this multiplication is a certain number of thousands.

To find the square of 725 we first write 0625 after the square of 7, making 490625. To this we add as many thousands as are represented by 7×5. $490625 + 35000 = 525625$.

Another method of finding these squares is by setting the numbers down as in the following illustration.

$$\begin{array}{r} 725 \\ 725 \\ \hline 525625 \end{array}$$

At once write 625 as the square of 25. Multiply 7 by 5, write 5 and carry 3; multiply 7 by 7, add 3, write 52.

Find the square of the following numbers by both of the foregoing methods.

1. 525	**3.** 825	**5.** 1225	**7.** 1625	**9.** 1825
2. 625	**4.** 1025	**6.** 1325	**8.** 1725	**10.** 1925

Exercise No. 378

Multiplying a Sum by a Difference

The algebraic product of $a + b$ and $a - b$ is $a^2 - b^2$. When numbers to be multiplied can be expressed as the sum of and the difference between two numbers, the product equals the square of the first minus the square of the second. Thus 63×57 may be expressed as $60 + 3$ multiplied by $60 - 3$. The product equals 60×60 minus 3×3. This comes to $3600 - 9$ or 3591.

There is no limit to the combinations of numbers for which this principle would hold true, but for practical purposes we may be satisfied to recognize those in which the units add to 10 and the tens have a difference of 1.

Multiply the following by this method.

1. 72×68	**4.** 101×119	**7.** 152×168
2. 83×77	**5.** 123×137	**8.** 173×187
3. 94×86	**6.** 146×154	**9.** 182×198

Exercise No. 379

Multiplying Mixed Numbers with Like Integers

When integers are alike in mixed numbers, as in $9\frac{1}{4} \times 9\frac{3}{4}$, their product is found by multiplying one integer by the other plus the sum of the two fractions; to this partial product add that obtained by multiplying together the two fractions.

$$9\frac{1}{4}$$
$$9\frac{3}{4}$$
$$\overline{90\frac{3}{16}}$$

$$8\frac{3}{4}$$
$$8\frac{5}{8}$$
$$\overline{76\frac{2}{3}}$$
$$\frac{5}{8}$$
$$\overline{77\frac{7}{24}}$$

In the illustrative example at the left, 9 is multiplied by $9 + \frac{1}{4} + \frac{3}{4}$, or 10. The product of this is 90, and to 90 is added the product of $\frac{1}{4}$ and $\frac{3}{4}$, or $\frac{3}{16}$.

In the second example 8 is multiplied by $8 + \frac{3}{4} + \frac{5}{8}$, or $9\frac{7}{12}$, producing $76\frac{2}{3}$. To this is added the product of $\frac{3}{4} \times \frac{5}{8}$, or $\frac{5}{8}$, making a total of $77\frac{7}{24}$.

Multiply the following.

1. $9\frac{1}{3} \times 9\frac{2}{3}$ **5.** $3\frac{1}{3} \times 3\frac{2}{3}$ **9.** $5\frac{1}{4} \times 5\frac{1}{2}$

2. $10\frac{3}{5} \times 10\frac{3}{5}$ **6.** $60\frac{3}{5} \times 60\frac{3}{5}$ **10.** $8\frac{3}{4} \times 8\frac{1}{3}$

3. $12\frac{5}{6} \times 12\frac{1}{2}$ **7.** $40\frac{3}{8} \times 40\frac{1}{4}$ **11.** $6\frac{5}{8} \times 6\frac{3}{8}$

4. $18\frac{1}{2} \times 18\frac{1}{3}$ **8.** $25\frac{3}{5} \times 25\frac{2}{5}$ **12.** $12\frac{1}{9} \times 12\frac{5}{9}$

Exercise No. 380

Multiplying by a Number Nearly Whole

Sometimes a multiplier lacks a single fractional unit of being a whole number. Examples would be $5\frac{2}{3}$, $6\frac{3}{4}$ and $7\frac{4}{5}$, which respectively lack $\frac{1}{3}$, $\frac{1}{4}$ and $\frac{1}{5}$ of being 6, 7 and 8. In cases of this kind raise the multiplier to the next larger whole number, and after multiplying the multiplicand by this number, subtract from the product the necessary fractional part of the multiplicand. Thus, to multiply 64 by $3\frac{7}{8}$, we multiply 64 by 4, obtaining 256, and from this we subtract $\frac{1}{8}$ of 64, or 8, arriving at a final result of 248.

Multiply by this method the following.

1. $48 \times 5\frac{3}{4}$ **4.** $250 \times 3\frac{4}{5}$ **7.** $180 \times 7\frac{9}{10}$

2. $75 \times 10\frac{2}{3}$ **5.** $522 \times 4\frac{8}{9}$ **8.** $720 \times 2\frac{11}{12}$

3. $136 \times 6\frac{5}{6}$ **6.** $672 \times 8\frac{6}{7}$ **9.** $342 \times 9\frac{5}{8}$

Exercise No. 381

Aliquot Parts in Division

The method of aliquot parts is as applicable to division as it is to multiplication. In ordinary cases we determine how many times the given divisor is contained exactly in some multiple of 10. We multiply the given dividend by the result of such division, and point off the product decimally in such a way as to express division by the proper multiple of 10. Thus, to divide 1840 by 25, we obtain a multiplier of 4 by dividing 25 into 100. Multiplying 1840 by 4 we get 7360, and dividing this decimally by 100 we obtain 73.60

$$6375 \div 7\tfrac{1}{2}$$

$$
\begin{array}{r}
6375 \\
2125 \\
\hline
850.0
\end{array}
$$

Another method of using aliquot parts is illustrated by the example shown above. The problem is to divide 6375 by $7\tfrac{1}{2}$. We note that $7\tfrac{1}{2}$ lacks one-third of itself of being 10. We therefore add one-third of itself to 6375 and divide the resulting sum decimally by 10.

Divide by the foregoing methods:

1. $580 \div 25$	**4.** $875 \div 250$	**7.** $1527 \div 150$
2. $750 \div 16\tfrac{2}{3}$	**5.** $640 \div 125$	**8.** $918 \div 15$
3. $450 \div 12\tfrac{1}{2}$	**6.** $435 \div 33\tfrac{1}{3}$	**9.** $582 \div 7\tfrac{1}{2}$

Exercise No. 382

Cubes of Numbers

The algebraic formula for the cube of the sum of two numbers, a and b, is $a^3 + 3a^2b + 3ab^2 + b^3$. This may be expressed as the cube of the first plus three times the square of the first multiplied by the second, plus three times the first multiplied by the square of the second plus the cube of the second.

By applying this formula it is not difficult to calculate mentally the cubes of numbers of two places. Suppose, for instance, that we want to find the cube of 26. We immediately annex the cube of 6 (216) to the cube of 2 (8), obtaining 8216. (Always allow three places for the cube of the second.) Multiplying 3×400 (square of 20) $\times 6$, we get 7200, which, added to 8216, makes 15416. Multiplying $3 \times 20 \times 36$ (square of 6) we obtain 2160, which, added to 15416 gives 17576 as the cube of 26.

Cubes may be readily written down from right to left by using a different method.

26^3	$6 \times 6 \times 6 = 216$	6
$\overline{17576}$	$(6 \times 6 \times 2 \times 3) + 21 = 237$	7
	$(6 \times 2 \times 2 \times 3) + 23 = 95$	5
	$(2 \times 2 \times 2) + 9 = 17$	17

All the necessary writing is shown on p.144 at the left. The method of making the calculation is analyzed at the right. The cube of 6 is 216, write 6 and carry 21. The square of 6 (36) multiplied by 2 (72) multiplied by 3 (216) plus 21 comes to 237, write 7 and carry 23. The product of 6 times the square of 2 (24) multiplied by 3 (72) plus 23 comes to 95, write 5 and carry 9. The cube of 2 is 8, which, added to 9, makes 17.

Before attempting the examples which follow the student ought to make himself thoroughly familiar with the cubes of the numbers from 1 to 9, so that he will not have to slow up to make such computations in the course of the example.

Find the cubes of the following numbers by both of the foregoing methods.

1. 14	4. 46	7. 65	10. 84	13. 95
2. 27	5. 59	8. 71	11. 86	14. 97
3. 33	6. 62	9. 73	12. 88	15. 99

Exercise No. 383
Algebraic Multiplication

Arithmetical products may be directly written down from right to left by using the method of cross-multiplication employed in algebra. A certain pattern is followed in multiplying each figure by every other figure. The operations are best explained by illustration.

$$\begin{array}{r} 47 \\ 26 \\ \hline 1222 \end{array} \qquad \begin{array}{r} 345 \\ 678 \\ \hline 234910 \end{array}$$

In the example at the left, $7 \times 6 = 42$, write 2 and carry 4; 4 plus 4×6 (28) plus 2×7 comes to 42, write 2 and carry 4; 4 plus 4×2 is 12, write 12. (It is best to start each part of the calculation with the carried number, which otherwise might not be easy to remember.)

In the second example, multiply 5×8; then 4×8 and 7×5; then 3×8, 6×5 and 4×7; then 3×7 and 6×4; finally 3×6. Carry as may be necessary.

Table IV
Prime and Composite Numbers

1 Prime	41 Prime	71 Prime	98 = 2 × 49
2 Prime	42 = 2 × 21	72 = 2 × 36	7 × 14
3 Prime	3 × 14	3 × 24	99 = 3 × 33
4 = 2 × 2	6 × 7	4 × 18	9 × 11
5 Prime	43 Prime	6 × 12	100 = 2 × 50
6 = 2 × 3	44 = 2 × 22	8 × 9	4 × 25
7 Prime	4 × 11	73 Prime	5 × 20
8 = 2 × 4	45 = 3 × 15	74 = 2 × 37	10 × 10
9 = 3 × 3	5 × 9	75 = 3 × 25	101 Prime
10 = 2 × 5	46 = 2 × 23	5 × 15	102 = 2 × 51
11 Prime	47 Prime	76 = 2 × 38	3 × 34
12 = 2 × 6	48 = 2 × 24	4 × 19	6 × 17
3 × 4	3 × 16	77 = 7 × 11	103 Prime
13 Prime	4 × 12	78 = 2 × 39	104 = 2 × 52
14 = 2 × 7	6 × 8	3 × 26	4 × 26
15 = 3 × 5	49 = 7 × 7	6 × 13	8 × 13
16 = 2 × 8	50 = 2 × 25	79 Prime	105 = 3 × 35
4 = 4	5 × 10	80 = 2 × 40	5 × 21
17 Prime	51 = 3 × 17	4 × 20	7 × 15
18 = 2 × 9	52 = 2 × 26	5 × 16	106 = 2 × 53
3 × 6	4 × 13	8 × 10	107 Prime
19 Prime	53 Prime	81 = 3 × 27	108 = 2 × 54
20 = 2 × 10	54 = 2 × 27	9 × 9	3 × 36
4 × 5	3 × 18	82 = 2 × 41	4 × 27
21 = 3 × 7	6 × 9	83 Prime	6 × 18
22 = 2 × 11	55 = 5 × 11	84 = 2 × 42	9 × 12
23 Prime	56 = 2 × 28	3 × 28	109 Prime
24 = 2 × 12	4 × 14	4 × 21	110 = 2 × 55
3 × 8	7 × 8	6 × 14	5 × 22
4 × 6	57 = 3 × 19	7 × 12	10 × 11
25 = 5 × 5	58 = 2 × 29	85 = 5 × 17	111 = 3 × 37
26 = 2 × 13	59 Prime	86 = 2 × 43	112 = 2 × 56
27 = 3 × 9	60 = 2 × 30	87 = 3 × 29	4 × 28
28 = 2 × 14	3 × 20	88 = 2 × 44	7 × 16
4 × 7	4 × 15	4 × 22	8 × 14
29 Prime	5 × 12	8 × 11	113 Prime
30 = 2 × 15	6 × 10	89 Prime	114 = 2 × 57
3 × 10	61 Prime	90 = 2 × 45	3 × 38
5 × 6	62 = 2 × 31	3 × 30	6 × 19
31 Prime	63 = 3 × 21	5 × 18	115 = 5 × 23
32 = 2 × 16	7 × 9	6 × 15	116 = 2 × 58
4 × 8	64 = 2 × 32	9 × 10	4 × 29
33 = 3 × 11	4 × 16	91 = 7 × 13	117 = 3 × 39
34 = 2 × 17	8 × 8	92 = 2 × 46	9 × 13
35 = 5 × 7	65 = 5 × 13	4 × 23	118 = 2 × 59
36 = 2 × 18	66 = 2 × 33	93 = 3 × 31	119 = 7 × 17
3 × 12	3 × 22	94 = 2 × 47	120 = 2 × 60
4 × 9	6 × 11	95 = 5 × 19	3 × 40
6 × 6	67 Prime	96 = 2 × 48	4 × 30
37 Prime	68 = 2 × 34	3 × 32	5 × 24
38 = 2 × 19	4 × 17	4 × 24	6 × 20
39 = 3 × 13	69 = 3 × 23	6 × 16	8 × 15
40 = 2 × 20	70 = 2 × 35	8 × 12	10 × 12
4 × 10	5 × 14	97 Prime	121 = 11 × 11
5 × 8	7 × 10		122 = 2 × 61

Table IV (Continued)

123 = 3 × 41	149 Prime	173 Prime	196 = 2 × 98
124 = 2 × 62	150 = 2 × 75	174 = 2 × 87	4 × 49
4 × 31	3 × 50	3 × 58	7 × 28
125 = 5 × 25	5 × 30	6 × 29	14 × 14
126 = 2 × 63	6 × 25	175 = 5 × 35	197 Prime
3 × 42	10 × 15	7 × 25	198 = 2 × 99
6 × 21	151 Prime	176 = 2 × 88	3 × 66
7 × 18	152 = 2 × 76	4 × 44	6 × 33
9 × 14	4 × 38	8 × 22	9 × 22
127 Prime	8 × 19	11 × 16	11 × 18
128 = 2 × 64	153 = 3 × 51	177 = 3 × 59	199 Prime
4 × 32	9 × 17	178 = 2 × 89	200 = 2 × 100
8 × 16	154 = 2 × 77	179 Prime	4 × 50
129 = 3 × 43	7 × 22	180 = 2 × 90	5 × 40
130 = 2 × 65	11 × 14	3 × 60	8 × 25
5 × 26	155 = 5 × 31	4 × 45	10 × 20
10 × 13	156 = 2 × 78	5 × 36	201 = 3 × 67
131 Prime	3 × 52	6 × 30	202 = 2 × 101
132 = 2 × 66	4 × 39	9 × 20	203 = 7 × 29
3 × 44	6 × 26	10 × 18	204 = 2 × 102
4 × 33	12 × 13	12 × 15	3 × 68
6 × 22	157 Prime	181 Prime	4 × 51
11 × 12	158 = 2 × 79	182 = 2 × 91	6 × 34
133 = 7 × 19	159 = 3 × 53	7 × 26	12 × 17
134 = 2 × 67	160 = 2 × 80	13 × 14	205 = 5 × 41
135 = 3 × 45	4 × 40	183 = 3 × 61	206 = 2 × 103
5 × 27	5 × 32	184 = 2 × 92	207 = 3 × 69
9 × 15	8 × 20	4 × 46	9 × 23
136 = 2 × 68	10 × 16	8 × 23	208 = 2 × 104
4 × 34	161 = 7 × 23	185 = 5 × 37	4 × 52
8 × 17	162 = 2 × 81	186 = 2 × 93	8 × 26
137 Prime	3 × 54	3 × 62	13 × 16
138 = 2 × 69	6 × 27	6 × 31	209 = 11 × 19
3 × 46	9 × 18	187 = 11 × 17	210 = 2 × 105
6 × 23	163 Prime	188 = 2 × 94	3 × 70
139 Prime	164 = 2 × 82	4 × 47	5 × 42
140 = 2 × 70	4 × 41	189 = 3 × 63	6 × 35
4 × 35	165 = 3 × 55	7 × 27	7 × 30
5 × 28	5 × 33	9 × 21	10 × 21
7 × 20	11 × 15	190 = 2 × 95	14 × 15
10 × 14	166 = 2 × 83	5 × 38	211 Prime
141 = 3 × 47	167 Prime	10 × 19	212 = 2 × 106
142 = 2 × 71	168 = 2 × 84	191 Prime	4 × 53
143 = 11 × 13	3 × 56	192 = 2 × 96	213 = 3 × 71
144 = 2 × 72	4 × 42	3 × 64	214 = 2 × 107
3 × 48	6 × 28	4 × 48	215 = 5 × 43
4 × 36	7 × 24	6 × 32	216 = 2 × 108
6 × 24	8 × 21	8 × 24	3 × 72
8 × 18	12 × 14	12 × 16	4 × 54
9 × 16	169 = 13 × 13	193 Prime	6 × 36
12 × 12	170 = 2 × 85	194 = 2 × 97	8 × 27
145 = 5 × 29	5 × 34	195 = 3 × 65	9 × 24
146 = 2 × 73	10 × 17	5 × 39	12 × 18
147 = 3 × 49	171 = 3 × 57	13 × 15	217 = 7 × 31
7 × 21	9 × 19		218 = 2 × 109
148 = 2 × 74	172 = 2 × 86		219 = 3 × 73
4 × 37	4 × 43		

Table IV (Continued)

220 = 2 × 110	240 = 2 × 120	261 = 3 × 87	283 Prime
4 × 55	3 × 80	9 × 29	284 = 2 × 142
5 × 44	4 × 60	262 = 2 × 131	4 × 71
10 × 22	5 × 48	263 Prime	285 = 3 × 95
11 × 20	6 × 40	264 2 × 132	5 × 57
221 = 13 × 17	8 × 30	3 × 88	15 × 19
222 = 2 × 111	10 × 24	4 × 66	286 = 2 × 143
3 × 74	12 × 20	6 × 44	11 × 26
6 × 37	15 × 16	8 × 33	13 × 22
223 Prime	241 Prime	11 × 24	287 = 7 × 41
224 = 2 × 112	242 = 2 × 121	12 × 22	288 = 2 × 144
4 × 56	11 × 22	265 = 5 × 53	3 × 96
7 × 32	243 = 3 × 81	266 = 2 × 133	4 × 72
8 × 28	9 × 27	7 × 38	6 × 48
14 × 16	244 = 2 × 122	14 × 19	8 × 36
225 = 3 × 75	4 × 61	267 = 3 × 89	9 × 32
5 × 45	245 = 5 × 49	268 = 2 × 134	12 × 24
9 × 25	7 × 35	4 × 67	16 × 18
15 × 15	246 = 2 × 123	269 Prime	289 = 17 × 17
226 = 2 × 113	3 × 82	270 = 2 × 135	290 = 2 × 145
227 Prime	6 × 41	3 × 90	5 × 58
228 = 2 × 114	247 = 13 × 19	5 × 54	10 × 29
3 × 76	248 = 2 × 124	6 × 45	291 = 3 × 97
4 × 57	4 × 62	9 × 30	292 = 2 × 146
6 × 38	8 × 31	10 × 27	4 × 73
12 × 19	249 = 3 × 83	15 × 18	293 Prime
229 Prime	250 = 2 × 125	271 Prime	294 = 2 × 147
230 = 2 × 115	5 × 50	272 = 2 × 136	3 × 98
5 × 46	10 × 25	4 × 68	6 × 49
10 × 23	251 Prime	8 × 34	7 × 42
231 = 3 × 77	252 = 2 × 126	16 × 17	14 × 21
7 × 33	3 × 84	273 = 3 × 91	295 = 5 × 59
11 × 21	4 × 63	7 × 39	296 = 2 × 148
232 = 2 × 116	6 × 42	13 × 21	4 × 74
4 × 58	7 × 36	274 = 2 × 137	8 × 37
8 × 29	9 × 28	275 = 5 × 55	297 = 3 × 99
233 Prime	12 × 21	11 × 25	9 × 33
234 = 2 × 117	14 × 18	276 = 2 × 138	11 × 27
3 × 78	253 = 11 × 23	3 × 92	298 = 2 × 149
6 × 39	254 = 2 × 127	4 × 69	299 = 13 × 23
9 × 26	255 = 3 × 85	6 × 46	300 = 2 × 150
13 × 18	5 × 51	12 × 23	3 × 100
235 = 5 × 47	15 × 17	277 Prime	4 × 75
236 = 2 × 118	256 = 2 × 128	278 = 2 × 139	5 × 60
4 × 59	4 × 64	279 = 3 × 93	6 × 50
237 = 3 × 79	8 × 32	9 × 31	10 × 30
238 = 2 × 119	16 × 16	280 = 2 × 140	12 × 25
7 × 34	257 Prime	4 × 70	15 × 20
14 × 17	258 = 2 × 129	5 × 56	301 = 7 × 43
239 Prime	3 × 86	7 × 40	302 = 2 × 151
	6 × 43	8 × 35	303 = 3 × 101
	259 = 7 × 37	10 × 28	304 = 2 × 152
	260 = 2 × 130	14 × 20	4 × 76
	4 × 65	281 Prime	8 × 38
	5 × 52	282 = 2 × 141	16 × 19
	10 × 26	3 × 94	305 = 5 × 61
	13 × 20	6 × 47	

Table IV (Continued)

306 = 2 × 153	*326* = 2 × 163	348 = 2 × 174	*368* = 2 × 184
3 × 102	327 = 3 × 109	3 × 116	4 × 92
6 × 51	328 = 2 × 164	4 × 87	8 × 46
9 × 34	4 × 82	6 × 58	16 × 23
17 × 18	8 × 41	12 × 29	369 = 3 × 123
307 Prime	329 = 7 × 47	349 Prime	9 × 41
308 = 2 × 154	*330* = 2 × 165	*350* = 2 × 175	370 = 2 × 185
4 × 77	3 × 110	5 × 70	5 × 74
7 × 44	5 × 66	7 × 50	10 × 37
11 × 28	6 × 55	10 × 35	371 = 5 × 53
14 × 22	10 × 33	14 × 25	372 = 2 × 186
309 = 3 × 103	11 × 30	351 = 3 × 117	3 × 124
310 = 2 × 155	15 × 22	9 × 39	4 × 93
5 × 62	331 Prime	13 × 27	6 × 62
10 × 31	332 = 2 × 166	*352* = 2 × 176	12 × 31
311 = Prime	4 × 83	4 × 88	373 Prime
312 = 2 × 156	333 = 3 × 111	8 × 44	*374* = 2 × 187
3 × 104	9 × 37	11 × 32	11 × 34
4 × 78	334 = 2 × 167	16 × 22	17 × 22
6 × 52	335 = 5 × 67	353 Prime	*375* = 3 × 125
8 × 39	*336* = 2 × 168	354 = 2 × 177	5 × 75
12 × 26	3 × 112	3 × 118	15 × 25
13 × 24	4 × 84	6 × 59	376 = 2 × 188
313 Prime	6 × 56	355 = 5 × 71	4 × 94
314 = 2 × 157	7 × 48	356 = 2 × 178	8 × 47
315 = 3 × 105	8 × 42	4 × 89	377 = 13 × 29
5 × 63	12 × 28	*357* = 3 × 119	*378* = 2 × 189
7 × 45	14 × 24	7 × 51	3 × 126
9 × 35	16 × 21	17 × 21	6 × 63
15 × 21	337 Prime	358 = 2 × 179	7 × 54
316 = 2 × 158	338 = 2 × 169	359 Prime	9 × 42
4 × 79	13 × 26	*360* = 2 × 180	14 × 27
317 Prime	339 = 3 × 113	3 × 120	18 × 21
318 = 2 × 159	*340* = 2 × 170	4 × 90	379 Prime
3 × 106	4 × 85	5 × 72	*380* = 2 × 190
6 × 53	5 × 68	6 × 60	4 × 95
319 = 11 × 29	10 × 34	8 × 45	5 × 76
320 = 2 × 160	17 × 20	9 × 40	10 × 38
4 × 80	341 = 11 × 31	10 × 36	19 × 20
5 × 64	*342* = 2 × 171	12 × 30	381 = 3 × 127
8 × 40	3 × 114	15 × 24	382 = 2 × 191
10 × 32	6 × 57	18 × 20	383 Prime
16 × 20	9 × 38	*361* = 19 × 19	*384* = 2 × 192
321 = 3 × 107	18 × 19	362 = 2 × 181	3 × 128
322 = 2 × 161	*343* = 7 × 49	363 = 3 × 121	4 × 96
7 × 46	344 = 2 × 172	11 × 33	6 × 64
14 × 23	4 × 86	364 = 2 × 182	8 × 48
323 = 17 × 19	8 × 43	4 × 91	12 × 32
324 = 2 × 162	*345* = 3 × 115	7 × 52	16 × 24
3 × 108	5 × 69	13 × 28	385 = 5 × 77
4 × 81	15 × 23	14 × 26	7 × 55
6 × 54	346 = 2 × 173	365 = 5 × 73	11 × 35
9 × 36	347 Prime	366 = 2 × 183	386 = 2 × 193
12 × 27		3 × 122	387 = 3 × 129
18 × 18		6 × 61	9 × 43
325 = 5 × 65		367 Prime	388 = 2 × 194
13 × 25			4 × 97

Table IV (Continued)

389　Prime	408 = 2 × 204	429 = 3 × 143	448 = 2 × 224
390 = 2 × 195	3 × 136	11 × 39	4 × 112
3 × 130	4 × 102	13 × 33	7 × 64
5 × 78	6 × 68	430 = 2 × 215	8 × 56
6 × 65	8 × 51	5 × 86	14 × 32
10 × 39	12 × 34	10 × 43	16 × 28
13 × 30	17 × 24	431　Prime	449　Prime
15 × 26	409　Prime	432 = 2 × 216	450 = 2 × 225
391 = 17 × 23	410 = 2 × 205	3 × 144	3 × 150
392 = 2 × 196	5 × 82	4 × 108	5 × 90
4 × 98	10 × 41	6 × 72	6 × 75
7 × 56	411 = 3 × 137	8 × 54	9 × 50
8 × 49	412 = 2 × 206	9 × 48	10 × 45
14 × 28	4 × 103	12 × 36	15 × 30
393 = 3 × 131	413 = 7 × 59	16 × 27	18 × 25
394 = 2 × 197	414 = 2 × 207	18 × 24	451 = 11 × 41
395 = 5 × 79	3 × 138	433　Prime	452 = 2 × 226
396 = 2 × 198	6 × 69	434 = 2 × 217	4 × 113
3 × 132	9 × 46	7 × 62	453 = 3 × 151
4 × 99	18 × 23	14 × 31	454 = 2 × 227
6 × 66	415 = 5 × 83	435 = 3 × 145	455 = 5 × 91
9 × 44	416 = 2 × 208	5 × 87	7 × 65
11 × 36	4 × 104	15 × 29	13 × 35
12 × 33	8 × 52	436 = 2 × 218	456 = 2 × 228
18 × 22	13 × 32	4 × 109	3 × 152
397　Prime	16 × 26	437 = 19 × 23	4 × 114
398 = 2 × 199	417 = 3 × 139	438 = 2 × 219	6 × 76
399 = 3 × 133	418 = 2 × 209	3 × 146	8 × 57
7 × 57	11 × 38	6 × 73	12 × 38
19 × 21	19 × 22	439　Prime	19 × 24
400 = 2 × 200	419　Prime	440 = 2 × 220	457　Prime
4 × 100	420 = 2 × 210	4 × 110	458 = 2 × 229
5 × 80	3 × 140	5 × 88	459 = 3 × 153
8 × 50	4 × 105	8 × 55	9 × 51
10 × 40	5 × 84	10 × 44	17 × 27
16 × 25	6 × 70	11 × 40	460 = 2 × 230
20 × 20	7 × 60	20 × 22	4 × 115
401　Prime	10 × 42	441 = 3 × 147	5 × 92
402 = 2 × 201	12 × 35	7 × 63	10 × 46
3 × 134	14 × 30	9 × 49	20 × 23
6 × 67	15 × 28	21 × 21	461　Prime
403 = 13 × 31	20 × 21	442 = 2 × 221	462 = 2 × 231
404 = 2 × 202	421　Prime	13 × 34	3 × 154
4 × 101	422 = 2 × 211	17 × 26	6 × 77
405 = 3 × 135	423 = 3 × 141	443　Prime	7 × 66
5 × 81	9 × 47	444 = 2 × 222	11 × 42
9 × 45	424 = 2 × 212	3 × 148	14 × 33
15 × 27	4 × 106	4 × 111	21 × 22
406 = 2 × 203	8 × 53	6 × 74	463　Prime
7 × 58	425 = 5 × 85	12 × 37	464 = 2 × 232
14 × 29	17 × 25	445 = 5 × 89	4 × 116
407 = 11 × 37	426 = 2 × 213	446 = 2 × 223	8 × 58
	3 × 142	447 = 3 × 149	16 × 29
	6 × 71		465 = 3 × 155
	427 = 7 × 61		5 × 93
	428 = 2 × 214		15 × 31
	4 × 107		466 = 2 × 233

Table IV (Continued)

467 Prime	486 = 2 × 243	*504* = 2 × 252	522 = 2 × 261
468 = 2 × 234	3 × 162	3 × 168	3 × 174
3 × 156	6 × 81	4 × 126	6 × 87
4 × 117	9 × 54	6 × 84	9 × 58
6 × 78	18 × 27	7 × 72	18 × 29
9 × 52	487 Prime	8 × 63	523 Prime
12 × 39	488 = 2 × 244	9 × 56	524 = 2 × 262
13 × 36	4 × 122	12 × 42	4 × 131
18 × 26	8 × 61	14 × 36	*525* = 3 × 175
469 = 7 × 67	489 = 3 × 163	18 × 28	5 × 105
470 = 2 × 235	490 = 2 × 245	21 × 24	7 × 75
5 × 94	5 × 98	505 = 5 × 101	15 × 35
10 × 47	7 × 70	*506* = 2 × 253	21 × 25
471 = 3 × 157	10 × 49	11 × 46	526 = 2 × 263
472 = 2 × 236	14 × 35	22 × 23	527 = 17 × 31
4 × 118	491 Prime	507 = 3 × 169	*528* = 2 × 264
8 × 59	492 = 2 × 246	13 × 39	3 × 176
473 = 11 × 43	3 × 164	508 = 2 × 254	4 × 132
474 = 2 × 237	4 × 123	4 × 127	6 × 88
3 × 158	6 × 82	509 Prime	8 × 66
6 × 79	12 × 41	510 = 2 × 255	11 × 48
475 = 5 × 95	493 = 17 × 29	3 × 170	12 × 44
19 × 25	494 = 2 × 247	5 × 102	16 × 33
476 = 2 × 238	13 × 38	6 × 85	22 × 24
4 × 119	19 × 26	10 × 51	*529* = 23 × 23
7 × 68	495 = 3 × 165	15 × 34	530 = 2 × 265
14 × 34	5 × 99	17 × 30	5 × 106
17 × 28	9 × 55	511 = 7 × 73	10 × 53
477 = 3 × 159	11 × 45	512 = 2 × 256	531 = 3 × 177
9 × 53	15 × 33	4 × 128	9 × 59
478 = 2 × 238	496 = 2 × 298	8 × 64	532 = 2 × 266
479 Prime	4 × 124	16 × 32	4 × 133
480 = 2 × 240	8 × 62	513 = 3 × 171	7 × 76
3 × 160	16 × 31	9 × 57	14 × 38
4 × 120	497 = 7 × 71	19 × 27	19 × 28
5 × 96	498 = 2 × 299	514 = 2 × 257	533 = 13 × 41
6 × 80	3 × 166	515 = 5 × 103	534 = 2 × 267
8 × 60	6 × 83	516 = 2 × 258	3 × 178
10 × 48	499 Prime	3 × 172	6 × 89
12 × 40	*500* = 2 × 250	4 × 129	535 = 5 × 107
15 × 32	4 × 125	6 × 86	536 = 2 × 268
16 × 30	5 × 100	12 × 43	4 × 134
20 × 24	10 × 50	517 = 11 × 47	8 × 67
481 = 13 × 37	20 × 25	518 = 2 × 259	537 = 3 × 179
482 = 2 × 241	501 = 3 × 167	7 × 74	538 = 2 × 269
483 = 3 × 161	502 = 2 × 251	14 × 37	539 = 7 × 77
7 × 69	503 Prime	519 = 3 × 173	11 × 49
21 × 23		520 = 2 × 260	
484 = 2 × 242		4 × 130	
4 × 121		5 × 104	
11 × 44		8 × 65	
22 × 22		10 × 52	
485 = 5 × 97		13 × 40	
		20 × 26	
		521 Prime	

Table IV (Continued)

540 = 2 × 270	558 = 2 × 279	*576* = 2 × 288	594 = 2 × 297
3 × 180	3 × 186	3 × 192	3 × 198
4 × 135	6 × 93	4 × 144	6 × 99
5 × 108	9 × 62	6 × 96	9 × 66
6 × 90	18 × 31	8 × 72	11 × 54
9 × 60	559 = 13 × 43	9 × 64	18 × 33
10 × 54	560 = 2 × 280	12 × 48	22 × 27
12 × 45	4 × 140	16 × 36	595 = 5 × 119
15 × 36	5 × 112	18 × 32	7 × 85
18 × 30	7 × 80	24 × 24	17 × 35
20 × 27	8 × 70	577 Prime	596 = 2 × 298
541 Prime	10 × 56	578 = 2 × 289	4 × 149
542 = 2 × 271	14 × 40	17 × 34	597 = 3 × 199
543 = 3 × 181	16 × 35	579 = 3 × 193	598 = 2 × 299
544 = 2 × 272	20 × 28	580 = 2 × 290	13 × 46
4 × 136	561 = 3 × 187	4 × 145	23 × 26
8 × 68	11 × 51	5 × 116	599 Prime
16 × 34	17 × 33	10 × 58	*600* = 2 × 300
17 × 32	562 = 2 × 281	20 × 29	3 × 200
645 = 5 × 109	563 Prime	581 = 7 × 83	4 × 150
546 = 2 × 273	564 = 2 × 282	582 = 2 × 291	5 × 120
3 × 182	3 × 188	3 × 194	6 × 100
6 × 91	4 × 141	6 × 97	8 × 75
7 × 78	6 × 94	583 = 11 × 53	10 × 60
13 × 42	12 × 47	584 = 2 × 292	12 × 50
14 × 39	565 = 5 × 113	4 × 146	15 × 40
21 × 26	566 = 2 × 283	8 × 73	20 × 30
547 Prime	567 = 3 × 189	585 = 3 × 195	24 × 25
548 = 2 × 274	7 × 81	5 × 117	601 Prime
4 × 137	9 × 63	9 × 65	602 = 2 × 301
549 = 3 × 183	21 × 27	13 × 45	7 × 86
9 × 61	568 = 2 × 284	15 × 39	14 × 43
550 = 2 × 275	4 × 142	586 = 2 × 293	603 = 3 × 201
5 × 110	8 × 71	587 Prime	9 × 67
10 × 55	569 Prime	588 = 2 × 294	604 = 2 × 302
11 × 50	570 = 2 × 285	3 × 196	4 × 151
22 × 25	3 × 190	4 × 147	605 = 5 × 121
551 = 19 × 29	5 × 114	6 × 98	11 × 55
552 = 2 × 276	6 × 95	7 × 84	606 = 2 × 303
3 × 184	10 × 57	12 × 49	3 × 202
4 × 138	15 × 38	14 × 42	6 × 101
6 × 92	19 × 30	21 × 28	607 Prime
8 × 69	571 Prime	589 = 19 × 31	608 = 2 × 304
12 × 46	572 = 2 × 286	590 = 2 × 295	1 × 152
23 × 24	4 × 143	5 × 118	8 × 76
553 = 7 × 79	11 × 52	10 × 59	16 × 38
554 = 2 × 277	13 × 44	591 = 3 × 197	19 × 32
555 = 3 × 185	22 × 26	592 = 2 × 296	609 = 3 × 203
5 × 111	573 = 3 × 191	4 × 148	7 × 87
15 × 37	574 = 2 × 287	8 × 74	21 × 29
556 = 2 × 278	7 × 82	16 × 37	610 = 2 × 305
4 × 139	14 × 41	593 Prime	5 × 122
557 Prime	*575* = 5 × 115		10 × 61
	23 × 25		611 = 13 × 47

Table IV (Concluded)

612 = 2 × 306	616 = 2 × 308	619 Prime	624 = 2 × 312
3 × 204	4 × 154	620 = 2 × 310	3 × 208
4 × 152	7 × 88	4 × 155	4× 156
6 × 102	8 × 77	5 × 124	6× 104
9 × 68	11 × 56	10 × 62	8 × 78
12 × 51	14 × 44	20 × 31	12 × 52
17 × 36	22 × 28	621 = 3 × 207	13 × 48
18 × 34	617 Prime	9 × 69	16 × 39
613 Prime	618 = 2 × 309	23 × 27	24 × 26
614 = 2 × 307	3 × 206	622 = 2 × 311	625 = 5 × 125
615 = 3 × 205	6 × 103	623 = 7 × 89	25 × 25
5 × 123			
15 × 41			

ANSWERS

The references at the head of each section are to the numbers of the exercises.

No. 1				
	30	70	69	53
	86	54	25	109
1. 32	42	110	81	65
2. 30	98	66	37	21
3. 29	26	22	93	77
4. 29	82	78	49	40
5. 29	38	34	105	96
6. 31	94	90	68	52
7. 31	50	53	24	108
8. 18	106	109	80	64
9. 37	62	65	36	48
10. 31	25	21	92	104
11. 25	81	77	20	60
12. 35	37	61	76	16
13. 34	93	17	32	72
14. 29	49	73	88	28
15. 26	105	29	44	84
16. 25	33	85	100	47
17. 30	89	41	56	103
18. 33	45	97	19	59
19. 27	101	60	75	15
20. 30	57	16	31	71
21. 33	13	72	87	55
22. 26	69	28	43	111
23. 28	32	84	99	67
24. 27	88		27	23
	44		83	79
	100	No. 3	39	35
No. 2	56		95	91
	40	**1.** 59	51	54
12	96	**2.** 51	107	110
68	52	**3.** 56	63	66
24	108	**4.** 70	26	22
80	64	**5.** 62	82	78
36	20	**6.** 55	38	62
92	76	**7.** 57	94	18
48	39	**8.** 59	50	74
104	95	**9.** 53	106	30
67	51	**10.** 51	34	86
23	107	**11.** 69	90	42
79	63	**12.** 58	46	98
35	47	**13.** 60	102	61
91	103	**14.** 65	58	17
19	59	**15.** 59	14	73
75	15	**16.** 61	70	29
31	71	**17.** 53	33	85
87	27	**18.** 53	89	
43	83		45	
99	46		101	No. 5
55	102	No. 4	57	
18	58		41	14
74	14	13	97	70

26	109	46	113	29
82	65	102	69	85
38	49	58	25	41
94	105	21	81	97
50	61	77	**37**	53
106	17	33	93	109
69	73	89	56	37
25	29	45	112	93
81	85	101	68	49
37	48	29	24	105
93	104	85	80	61
21	60	41	64	17
77	16	97	20	73
33	72	53	76	36
89	56	109	32	92
45	112	65	88	48
101	68	28	44	104
57	24	84	100	60
20	80	40	63	44
76	36	96	19	100
32	92	52	75	56
88	55	108	31	112
44	111	36	87	68
100	67	92		24
28	23	48	**No. 7**	80
84	79	104		43
40	63	60	16	99
96	19	16	72	55
52	75	72	28	111
108	31	35	84	67
64	87	91	40	51
27	43	47	96	107
83	99	103	52	63
39	62	59	108	19
95	18	43	71	75
51	74	99	27	31
107	30	55	83	87
35	86	111	39	50
91		67	95	106
47		23	23	62
103	**No. 6**	79	79	18
59		42	35	74
15	15	98	91	58
71	71	54	47	114
34	27	110	103	70
90	83	66	59	26
46	39	50	22	82
102	95	106	78	38
58	51	62	34	94
42	107	18	90	57
98	70	74	46	113
54	26	30	102	69
110	82	86	30	25
66	38	49	86	81
22	94	105	42	65
78	22	61	98	21
41	78	17	54	77
97	34	73	110	33
53	90	57	66	89

45	37	30	113	98
101	93	86	69	26
64	49	42	53	82
20	105	98	109	38
76	61	54	65	94
32	45	110	21	50
88	101	73	77	106
No. 8	57	29	33	62
(*Same as*	113	85	89	25
No. 1)	69	41	52	81
No. 9	25	97	108	37
17	81	25	64	93
73	44	81	20	49
29	100	37	76	105
85	56	93	60	33
41	112	49	116	89
97	68	105	72	45
53	52	61	28	101
109	108	24	84	57
72	64	80	40	113
28	20	36	96	69
84	76	92	59	32
40	32	48	115	88
96	88	104	71	44
24	51	32	27	100
80	107	88	83	56
36	63	44	67	112
92	19	100	23	40
48	75	56	79	96
104	59	112	35	52
60	115	68	91	108
23	71	31	47	64
79	27	87	103	20
35	83	43	66	76
91	39	99	22	39
47	95	55	78	95
103	58	111	34	51
31	114	39	90	107
87	70	95	**No. 11**	63
43	26	51	(*Same as*	47
99	82	107	*No. 3*)	103
55	66	63		59
111	22	19	**No. 12**	115
67	78	75		71
30	34	38	19	27
86	90	94	75	83
42	46	50	31	46
98	102	106	87	102
54	65	62	43	58
110	21	46	99	114
38	77	102	55	70
94	33	58	111	54
50	89	114	74	110
106		70	30	66
62	**No. 10**	26	86	22
18		82	42	78
74	18	45		34
	74	101		90
		57		53

	No. 14		14. 656	
109		84	15. 858	61
65	20	47		117
21	76	103		73
77	32	59	No. 16	29
61	88	115		85
117	44	71		48
73	100	55	21	104
29	56	111	77	60
85	112	67	33	116
41	75	23	89	72
97	31	79	45	56
60	87	35	101	112
116	43	91	57	68
72	99	54	113	24
28	27	110	76	80
84	83	66	32	36
68	39	22	88	92
24	95	78	44	55
80	51	62	100	111
36	107	118	28	67
92	63	74	84	23
48	26	30	40	79
104	82	86	96	63
67	38	42	52	119
23	94	98	108	75
79	50	61	64	31
35	106	117	27	87
91	34	73	83	43
	90	29	39	99
	46	85	95	62
	102	69	51	118
	58	25	107	74
No. 13	114	81	35	30
	70	37	91	86
1. 365	33	93	47	70
2. 268	89	49	103	26
3. 371	45	105	59	82
4. 433	101	68	115	38
5. 257	57	24	71	94
6. 327	113	80	34	50
7. 209	41	36	90	106
8. 270	97	92	46	69
9. 287	53		102	25
10. 410	109		58	81
11. 257	65	**No. 15**	114	37
12. 404	21		42	93
13. 231	77	**1.** 620	98	
14. 217	40	**2.** 777	54	
15. 311	96	**3.** 716	110	**No. 17**
16. 303	52	**4.** 562	66	
17. 254	108	**5.** 432	22	**1.** 1059
18. 237	64	**6.** 590	78	**2.** 1055
19. 308	48	**7.** 624	41	**3.** 903
20. 343	104	**8.** 716	97	**4.** 963
21. 350	60	**9.** 885	53	**5.** 897
22. 360	116	**10.** 828	109	**6.** 1113
23. 308	72	**11.** 424	65	**7.** 1067
24. 271	28	**12.** 592	49	**8.** 759
25. 341		**13.** 535	105	**9.** 994

10. 932

No. 18

22
78
34
90
46
102
58
114
77
33
89
45
101
29
85
41
97
53
109
65
28
84
40
96
52
108
36
92
48
104
60
116
72
35
91
47
103
59
115
43
99
55
111
67
23
79
42
98
54
110
66
50
106
62

118
74
30
86
49
105
61
117
73
57
113
69
25
81
37
93
56
112
68
24
80
64
120
76
32
88
44
100
63
119
75
31
87
71
27
83
39
95
51
107
70
26
82
38
94

No. 19

1. 12
2. 34
3. 21
4. 56
5. 33
6. 78
7. 12
8. 13
9. 12
10. 21

11. 7
12. 34
13. 52
14. 11
15. 52

No. 20

1. 28
2. 28
3. 12
4. 19
5. 15
6. 26
7. 19
8. 18
9. 48
10. 21
11. 39
12. 17
13. 26
14. 58
15. 28
16. 18
17. 29
18. 19
19. 29

No. 21

23
79
35
91
47
103
59
115
78
34
90
46
102
30
86
42
98
54
110
66
29
85
41
97
53
109
37

93
49
105
61
117
73
36
92
48
104
60
116
44
100
56
112
68
24
80
43
99
55
111
67
51
107
63
119
75
31
87
50
106
62
118
74
58
114
70
26
82
38
94
57
113
69
25
81
65
121
77
33
89
45
101
64
120
76
32

88
72
28
84
40
96
52
108
71
27
83
39
95

No. 22

1. 294
2. 234
3. 414
4. 358
5. 379
6. 381
7. 370
8. 347
9. 221
10. 374

No. 23

1. 521
2. 213
3. 233
4. 321
5. 331
6. 313
7. 252
8. 412
9. 212
10. 130
11. 122
12. 441
13. 432
14. 351
15. 221

No. 24

24
80
36
92
48

104	115	31	91	**22.** 437
60	71	87	47	**23.** 722
116	27	43	103	**24.** 109
79	83	99	66	**25.** 515
35	39	55	122	**26.** 209
91	95	111	78	**27.** 336
47	58	39	34	**28.** 107
103	114	95	90	**29.** 868
31	70	51	74	**30.** 419
87	26	107	30	
43	82	63	86	
99	66	119	42	**No. 28**
55	122	75	98	
111	78	38	54	26
67	34	94	110	82
30	90	50	73	38
86	46	106	29	94
42	102	62	85	50
98	65	118	41	106
54	121	46	97	62
110	77	102		118
38	33	58		81
94	89	114		37
50	73	70		93
106	29	26		49
62	85	82	**No. 26**	105
118	41	45		33
74	97	101	**1.** $655.71	89
37	53	57	**2.** $751.32	45
93	109	113	**3.** $604.24	101
49	72	69	**4.** $577.21	57
105	28	53	**5.** $718.69	113
61	84	109	**6.** $769.64	69
117	40	65	**7.** $488.04	32
45	96	121	**8.** $691.93	88
101		77		44
57		33		100
113	**No. 25**	89	**No. 27**	56
69		52		112
25	25	108	**1.** 215	40
81	81	64	**2.** 415	96
44	37	120	**3.** 209	52
100	93	76	**4.** 329	108
56	49	60	**5.** 778	64
112	105	116	**6.** 109	120
68	61	72	**7.** 214	76
52	117	28	**8.** 248	39
108	80	84	**9.** 128	95
64	36	40	**10.** 237	51
120	92	96	**11.** 403	107
76	48	59	**12.** 106	63
32	104	115	**13.** 125	119
88	32	71	**14.** 125	47
51	88	27	**15.** 136	103
107	44	83	**16.** 204	59
63	100	67	**17.** 109	115
119	56	123	**18.** 143	71
75	112	79	**19.** 107	27
59	68	35	**20.** 308	
			21. 309	

83	83	110	35	118
46	39	66	91	74
102	95	122	47	30
58	51	78	103	86
114	107	62	59	70
70	63	118	115	126
54	119	74	71	82
110	82	30	34	38
66	38	86	90	94
122	94	42	46	50
78	50	98	102	106
34	106	61	58	69
90	34	117	114	125
53	90	73	42	81
109	46	29	98	37
65	102	85	54	93
121	58	69	110	79
77	114	125	66	33
61	70	81	112	89
117	33	37	78	45
73	89	93	41	101
29	45	49	97	57
85	101	105	53	113
41	57	68	109	76
97	113	124	65	32
60	41	80	121	88
116	97	36	49	44
72	53	92	105	100
28	109	76	61	
84	65	32	117	
68	121	88	73	
124	77	44	29	**No. 31**
80	40	100	85	
36	96	56	48	**1.** 621
92	52	112	104	**2.** 585
48	108	75	60	**3.** 687
104	54	31	116	**4.** 647
67	120	86	72	**5.** 630
123	48	43	56	**6.** 605
79	104	99	112	**7.** 570
35	60		68	**8.** 671
91	116		124	**9.** 625
75	72		80	**10.** 624
31	28	**No. 30**	36	
87	84		92	
43	47	28	55	
99	103	84	111	**No. 32**
55	59	40	67	
111	115	96	123	**1.** 161
74	71	52	79	**2.** 292
30	55	108	63	**3.** 71
86	111	64	119	**4.** 191
42	67	120	75	**5.** 171
98	123	83	31	**6.** 64
	79	39	87	**7.** 252
No. 29	35	95	43	**8.** 197
	91	51	99	**9.** 623
27	64	107	62	**10.** 284

11. 94
12. 387
13. 170
14. 61
15. 593
16. 195
17. 394
18. 295
19. 492
20. 681

No. 33

1. 465
2. 579
3. 164
4. 186
5. 153
6. 48
7. 489
8. 186
9. 488
10. 377
11. 329
12. 469
13. 288
14. 56
15. 216
16. 184
17. 249
18. 77
19. 289
20. 169

No. 34

1. $995.69
2. $1044.85
3. $954.07
4. $1002.63
5. $994.32
6. $897.80
7. $1122.66
8. $1051.42

No. 35

1. 395
2. 297
3. 92
4. 299
5. 298
6. 195
7. 298
8. 399
9. 494

10. 497
11. 296
12. 94
13. 495
14. 294
15. 299
16. 198
17. 197
18. 397
19. 293
20. 692
21. 198
22. 294
23. 596
24. 99
25. 395

No. 36

1. 985
2. 987
3. 975
4. 1008
5. 953
6. 1011
7. 1042
8. 1032
9. 1095
10. 1012

No. 37

1. 347
2. 189
3. 349
4. 78
5. 107
6. 259
7. 189
8. 119
9. 66
10. 88
11. 215
12. 178
13. 178
14. 9
15. 227
16. 100
17. 114
18. 249
19. 234
20. 29
21. 298
22. 284
23. 38
24. 376
25. 129

No. 38

1. $42357.49
2. $57112.34
3. $54738.19
4. $62369.15
5. $70468.35
6. $63801.69

No. 39

1. $4.35
2. $5.59
3. $ .94
4. $1.48
5. $6.92
6. $7.63
7. $2.31
8. $6.84
9. $3.70
10. $2.76
11. $2.29
12. $6.76
13. $3.59
14. $5.96
15. $1.56
16. $3.89
17. $2.68
18. $6.92
19. $3.49
20. $5.97

No. 40

(*Same as
No. 13*)

No. 41

1. $95513.02
2. $102635.78
3. $98506.46
4. $117398.69
5. $95153.78
6. $99073.91

No. 42

(*Same as
No. 39*)

No. 43

1. $ .93
2. $1.20

3. $2.81
4. $ .65
5. $1.96
6. $5.84
7. $2.95
8. $1.65
9. $2.24
10. $ .71
11. $1.89
12. $ .73
13. $1.23
14. $1.63
15. $1.71
16. $2.48
17. $1.86
18. $1.94
19. $2.45
20. $1.63

No. 44

(*Same as
No. 43*)

No. 45

2
114
26
138
50
162
74
186
112
24
136
48
160
16
128
40
152
64
176
88
14
126
38
150
62
174
30
142
54
166
78

190	124	174	228	336
102	36	63	52	160
28	148	231	276	384
140	60	99	100	208
52	172	267	324	144
164	98	135	148	368
76	10	87	372	192
188	122	255	224	16
44	34	123	48	240
156	146	291	272	64
68		159	96	288
180	**No. 46**	27	320	140
92		195	32	364
4	3	84	256	188
116	171	252	80	12
42	39	120	304	236
154	207	288	128	172
66	75	156	352	396
178	243	108	176	220
90	111	276	28	44
58	279	144	252	268
170	168	12	76	92
82	36	180	300	316
194	204	48	124	168
106	72	216	348	392
18	240	105	60	216
130	24	273	284	40
56	192	141	108	264
168	60	9	332	200
80	228	177	156	24
192	96	129	380	248
104	264	297	204	72
72	132	165	56	292
184	21	33	280	120
96	189	201	104	344
8	57	69	328	196
120	225	237	152	20
32	93	126	376	244
144	261	294	88	68
70	45	162	312	296
182	213	30	136	
94	81	198	360	
6	249	150	184	**No. 48**
118	117	18	8	
86	285	186	232	**1.** $3433540.07
198	153	54	84	**2.** $2509179.07
110	42	222	308	**3.** $3688667.60
22	210	90	132	**4.** $3251326.81
134	78	258	356	**5.** $3449296.55
46	246	147	180	**6.** $3353169.99
158	114	15	116	
84	282	183	340	
196	66	51	164	**No. 49**
108	234	219	388	
20	102		212	**1.** $18.53
132	270	**No. 47**	36	**2.** $25.66
100	138		260	**3.** $23.95
12	6	4	112	**4.** $14.78

Column 1

5. $41.76
6. $38.38
7. $15.74
8. $42.95
9. $60.76
10. $71.19
11. $66.57
12. $59.85
13. $93.72
14. $80.90
15. $75.68
16. $61.52

No. 50

5
285
65
345
125
405
185
465
280
60
340
120
400
40
320
100
380
160
440
220
35
315
95
375
155
435
75
355
135
415
195
475
255
70
350
130
410
190
470
110
390

Column 2

170
450
230
10
290
105
385
165
445
225
145
425
205
485
265
45
325
140
420
200
480
260
180
460
240
20
300
80
360
175
455
235
15
295
215
495
275
55
335
115
395
210
490
270
50
330
250
30
310
90
370
150
430
245
25
305
85
365

Column 3

No. 51

(Same as No. 49)

No. 52

6
342
78
414
150
486
222
558
336
72
408
144
480
48
384
120
456
192
528
264
42
378
114
450
186
522
90
426
162
498
234
570
306
84
420
156
492
228
564
132
468
204
540
276
12
348
126
462
198
534
270

Column 4

2
3
43
21
54
28
18
354
258
594
330
66
402
138
474
252
588
324
60
396
300
36
372
108
444
180
516
294
30
366
102
438

No. 53

7
399
91
483
175
567

Column 5

203
595
287
679
371
63
455
196
588
280
672
364
252

644	**12.** $55.60	712	**No. 59**	639
336	**13.** $97.15	360		243
28	**14.** $73.69	232	**1.** 795	747
420	**15.** $61.63	680	**2.** 682	351
112	**16.** $68.20	328	**3.** 564	855
504		776	**4.** 814	459
245		424	**5.** 598	126
637	**No. 56**	72	**6.** 924	630
329		520	**7.** 810	234
21	8	224	**8.** 946	738
413	456	672	**9.** 1032	342
301	104	320	**10.** 912	846
693	552	768	**11.** 901	198
385	200	416	**12.** 621	702
77	648	288	**13.** 665	306
469	296	736	**14.** 308	810
161	744	384	**15.** 962	414
553	448	32	**16.** 714	18
294	96	480	**17.** 1008	522
686	544	128	**18.** 364	189
378	192	576	**19.** 736	693
70	640	280	**20.** 782	297
462	64	728	**21.** 855	801
350	512	376	**22.** 864	405
42	160	24	**23.** 865	261
434	608	472	**24.** 988	765
126	256	344	**25.** 667	369
518	704	792		873
210	352	440		477
602	56	88	**No. 60**	81
343	504	536		585
35	152	184	9	252
427	600	632	513	756
119	248	336	117	360
511	696	784	621	864
	120	432	225	468
	568	80	729	324
No. 54	216	528	333	828
	664	400	837	432
1. $6537136.94	312	48	504	36
2. $6295852.28	760	496	108	540
3. $6328194.91	408	144	612	144
4. $5945296.77	112	592	216	648
	560	240	720	315
	208	688	72	819
No. 55	656	392	572	423
	304	40	180	27
1. $19.76	752	488	684	531
2. $18.86	176	136	288	387
3. $44.51	624	584	792	891
4. $26.39	272		396	495
5. $41.42	720	**No. 57**	63	99
6. $6.20	368	(*Same as*	567	603
7. $12.22	16	*No. 15*)	171	207
8. $19.63	464		675	711
9. $87.27	168	**No. 58**	279	378
10. $84.51	616	(*Same as*	783	882
11. $71.61	264	*No. 55*)	135	486

90	374	**No. 62**	**2.** $836.87
594	990		**3.** $666.99
450	506	**1.** $11230083.55	**4.** $829.97
54	22	**2.** $10797546.08	**5.** $634.22
558	608	**3.** $8876665.99	**6.** $827.43
162	231	**4.** $8230948.08	**7.** $857.76
666	847		**8.** $527.72
270	363		**9.** $418.44
774	979	**No. 63**	**10.** $906.92
441	495		**11.** $447.71
45	319	**1.** $47.65	**12.** $586.87
549	935	**2.** $6.21	**13.** $407.46
153	451	**3.** $79.61	**14.** $510.63
657	1067	**4.** $34.74	**15.** $533.62
	583	**5.** $14.68	**16.** $663.85
	99	**6.** $27.74	
No. 61	715	**7.** $27.93	
11	308	**8.** $21.85	**No. 68**
627	924	**9.** $54.46	
143	440	**10.** $13.83	*(Same as No. 17)*
759	1056	**11.** $36.49	
275	572	**12.** $4.46	
891	396	**13.** $50.47	**No. 69**
407	1012	**14.** $8.53	
1023	528	**15.** $27.16	*(Same as No. 67)*
616	44	**16.** $39.87	
132	660		
748	176		**No. 71**
264	792	**No. 65**	
880	385	*(Same as No. 63)*	**1.** $276.69
88	1001		**2.** $855.51
704	517		**3.** $682.90
220	33	**No. 66**	**4.** $520.36
836	649		**5.** $773.79
352	473	**1.** 1827	**6.** $891.54
968	1089	**2.** 1705	**7.** $326.93
484	605	**3.** 1170	**8.** $245.59
77	121	**4.** 1376	**9.** $371.93
693	737	**5.** 2511	**10.** $471.54
209	253	**6.** 2624	**11.** $386.88
825	869	**7.** 3772	**12.** $330.44
341	462	**8.** 1200	**13.** $878.62
957	1078	**9.** 1537	**14.** $696.89
165	594	**10.** 1235	**15.** $770.20
781	110	**11.** 1408	**16.** $674.87
297	726	**12.** 1428	
913	550	**13.** 1407	
429	66	**14.** 1408	**No. 72**
1045	682	**15.** 2016	
561	198	**16.** 2418	*(Same as No. 22)*
154	814	**17.** 3772	
770	330	**18.** 1164	
286	946	**19.** 2015	**No. 73**
902	539	**20.** 2592	
418	55		**1.** 755717535
1034	671		**2.** 756410013
242	187	**No. 67**	**3.** 824293224
858	803	**1.** $846.98	**4.** 824985702

5. 3674994324	144	720	**2.** 13361
6. 1167178458	816	192	**3.** 25543
7. 1236433047	288	864	**4.** 22632
8. 6091457406	960	420	**5.** 37893
9. 1690209807	96	1092	**6.** 34323
10. 1752668607	768	564	**7.** 52643
11. 1511041308	240	36	**8.** 45201
12. 3675686802	912	708	**9.** 68302
13. 1306128921	384	516	**10.** 62693
14. 1031412036	1056	1188	**11.** 19602
15. 1442533509	528	660	**12.** 12312
	84	132	**13.** 77922
	756	804	**14.** 33033
No. 74	228	276	**15.** 25662
	900	948	**16.** 12831
1. 1536	372	504	**17.** 16086
2. 4606	1044	1176	**18.** 20274
3. 2646	180	648	**19.** 22263
4. 1495	852	120	**20.** 47583
5. 5313	324	792	**21.** 44896
6. 3230	996	600	
7. 7347	468	72	
8. 4814	1140	744	**No. 81**
9. 4284	612	216	
10. 1295	168	888	**1.** 123782280
11. 6624	840	360	**2.** 123895704
12. 1624	312	1032	**3.** 135014592
13. 1886	984	588	**4.** 135128016
14. 3618	456	60	**5.** 601943392
15. 5494	1128	732	**6.** 191177264
16. 3861	264	204	**7.** 202520776
17. 3344	936	876	**8.** 997746448
18. 8608	408		**9.** 276846856
19. 1612	1080	**No. 78**	**10.** 287077256
20. 2655	552		**11.** 247500064
	24	(*Same as No. 34*)	**12.** 602056816
	696		**13.** 213936568
No. 75	252	**No. 79**	**14.** 168939488
	924		**15.** 236278872
(*Same as No. 71*)	396	**1.** $451.84	
	1068	**2.** $189.86	
	540	**3.** $343.97	**No. 82**
No. 76	348	**4.** $352.59	
	1020	**5.** $188.21	(*Same as No. 38*)
(*Same as No. 26*)	492	**6.** $145.71	
	1164	**7.** $291.97	**No. 83**
	636	**8.** $664.63	
No. 77	108	**9.** $136.68	**1.** $451.84
	780	**10.** $86.14	**2.** $189.86
12	336	**11.** $440.45	**3.** $343.97
684	1008	**12.** $221.48	**4.** $352.59
156	480	**13.** $196.63	**5.** $188.21
828	1152	**14.** $146.23	**6.** $145.71
300	624	**15.** $586.21	**7.** $291.97
972	432	**16.** $568.49	**8.** $664.63
444	1104		**9.** $136.68
1116	576	**No. 80**	**10.** $86.14
672	48		**11.** $440.45
		1. 17081	

12. $221.48
13. $196.63
14. $146.23
15. $586.21
16. $568.49

No. 84

1. 19584
2. 23793
3. 28288
4. 24466
5. 17344
6. 21483
7. 24208
8. 21346
9. 25164
10. 12691
11. 17138
12. 21918
13. 30702
14. 36206
15. 33355
16. 17199
17. 27846
18. 31003
19. 29120
20. 33948
21. 16238

No. 86

1. $95513.02
2. $102635.78
3. $98506.46
4. $117398.69
5. $95153.78
6. $99073.91

No. 89

1. 170810
2. 133610
3. 255430
4. 226320
5. 378930
6. 343230
7. 526430
8. 452010
9. 683020
10. 626930
11. 196020
12. 123120
13. 779220
14. 330330

15. 256620
16. 128310
17. 160860
18. 202740
19. 222630
20. 465830
21. 448960

No. 90

13
741
169
897
325
1053
481
1209
728
156
884
312
1040
104
832
260
988
416
1144
572
91
819
247
975
403
1131
195
923
351
1079
507
1235
663
182
910
338
1066
494
1222
286
1014
442
1170
598
26
754
273

1001
429
1157
585
377
1105
533
1261
689
117
845
364
1092
520
1248
676
468
1196
624
52
780
208
936
455
1183
611
39
767
559
1287
715
143
871
299
1027
546
1274
702
130
858
650
78
806
234
962
390
1118
637
65
793
221
949

No. 91

(Same as No. 48)

No. 93

1. 195840
2. 237930
3. 282880
4. 244660
5. 173440
6. 214830
7. 242080
8. 213460
9. 251640
10. 126910
11. 171380
12. 219180
13. 307020
14. 362060
15. 333550
16. 171990
17. 278460
18. 310030
19. 291200
20. 339480
21. 162380

No. 94

1. 135025095
2. 135148821
3. 147277608
4. 147401334
5. 656616308
6. 208541386
7. 220915199
8. 1088369102
9. 301992119
10. 303151719
11. 269979836
12. 656740034
13. 233367857
14. 184383812
15. 257739453

No. 95

(Same as No. 54)

No. 97

1. 11211
2. 24642
3. 40051
4. 57902
5. 77691
6. 92412
7. 29432

8. 21311	**9.** 287
9. 35742	**10.** 410
10. 52151	**11.** 257
11. 71002	**12.** 404
12. 91791	**13.** 231
13. 25521	**14.** 217
14. 48155	**15.** 311
15. 24442	**16.** 303
16. 49184	**17.** 254
17. 76146	**18.** 237
18. 44844	**19.** 308
19. 37296	**20.** 343
20. 97902	**21.** 350
21. 39693	**22.** 360
	23. 308

No. 99

1. $11230083.55
2. $10797546.08
3. $8876665.99
4. $8230948.08

24. 271
25. 341

No. 101

1. 36156
2. 59290
3. 80618
4. 22869
5. 36696
6. 52624
7. 71918
8. 93555
9. 97856
10. 103972
11. 108988
12. 84058
13. 103474
14. 108580
15. 79165
16. 57318
17. 65778
18. 77744
19. 91086
20. 35547
21. 80690

No. 103

1. 365
2. 268
3. 371
4. 433
5. 257
6. 327
7. 209
8. 270

No. 105

1. 116081
2. 142272
3. 165481
4. 107512
5. 132181
6. 159372
7. 156996
8. 191522
9. 181692
10. 217894
11. 110564
12. 110940
13. 121598
14. 120273
15. 134316
16. 120990
17. 113970
18. 145262
19. 122811
20. 139635
21. 144284

No. 106

14
798
182
966
350
1134
518
1302
784
168

952
336
1120
112
896
280
1064
448
1232
616
98
882
266
1050
434
1218
210
994
378
1162
546
1330
714
196
980
364
1148
532
1316
308
1092
476
1260
644
28
812
294
1078
462
1246
630
406
1190
574
1358
742
126
910
392
1176
560
1344
728
504
1288
672
56
840

224
1008
490
1274
658
42
826
602
1386
770
154
938
322
1106
588
1372
756
140
924
700
84
868
252
1036
420
1204
686
70
854
238
1022

No. 107

(*Same as No. 17*)

No. 109

1. 136004
2. 229024
3. 268746
4. 128064
5. 160446
6. 236496
7. 195853
8. 223096
9. 368063
10. 145673
11. 187146
12. 305283
13. 355096
14. 291014
15. 348928
16. 145728
17. 336414
18. 395324

19. 430265
20. 247275
21. 575276

No. 110

1. 146267910
2. 146401938
3. 159540624
4. 159674652
5. 711289224
6. 225905508
7. 239309622
8. 1178991756
9. 327137382
10. 339226182
11. 292459608
12. 711423252
13. 252799146
14. 199628136
15. 279200034

No. 111

(Same as No. 26)

No. 113

1. 164232
2. 227238
3. 301464
4. 377910
5. 456576
6. 497502
7. 658752
8. 172104
9. 243320
10. 279396
11. 354252
12. 427652
13. 484432
14. 588078
15. 671944
16. 175392
17. 173514
18. 257237
19. 341968
20. 429525
21. 519302

No. 115

(Same as No. 34)

No. 118

(Same as No. 38)

No. 119

15
855
195
1035
375
1215
555
1395
840
180
1020
360
1200
120
960
300
1140
480
1320
660
105
945
285
1125
465
1305
225
1065
405
1245
585
1425
765
210
1050
390
1230
570
1410
330
1170
510
1350
690
30
870
315
1155
495
1335
675

435
1275
615
1455
795
135
975
420
1260
600
1440
780
540
1380
720
60
900
240
1080
525
1365
705
45
885
645
1485
825
165
1005
345
1185
630
1470
810
150
990
750
90
930
270
1110
450
1290
735
75
915
255
1095

No. 120

(Same as No. 41)

No. 122

(Same as No. 48)

No. 123

1. 157510725
2. 157655055
3. 171803640
4. 171947970
5. 765962140
6. 243269630
7. 257704045
8. 1269714410
9. 352282645
10. 365300645
11. 314939380
12. 766106470
13. 272230435
14. 214972460
15. 300660615

No. 124

(Same as No. 54)

No. 126

(Same as No. 62)

No. 128

(Same as No. 38)

No. 131

16
912
208
1104
400
1296
92
1488
896
192
1088
384
1280
128
1024
320
1216
512
1408
704
112
1008

304	368	340	51
1200	1264	1292	1003
496	672	544	731
1392	1568	1496	1683
240	864	748	935
1136	160	119	187
432	1056	1071	1139
1328	800	323	391
624	96	1275	1343
1520	992	527	714
816	288	1479	1666
224	1184	255	918
1120	480	1207	170
416	1376	459	1122
1312	784	1411	850
608	80	663	102
1504	976	1615	1054
352	272	867	306
1248	1168	238	1258
544		1190	510
1440		442	1462
736	**No. 132**	1394	833
32		646	85
928	**1.** 168753540	1598	1037
336	**2.** 168908172	374	289
1232	**3.** 184066656	1326	1241
528	**4.** 184221288	578	
1424	**5.** 820635056	1530	
720	**6.** 260633752	782	**No. 141**
464	**7.** 276098468	34	
1360	**8.** 1360237064	996	**1.** 179996355
656	**9.** 377427908	357	**2.** 180161289
1552	**10.** 391375108	1309	**3.** 196329672
848	**11.** 337419152	561	**4.** 196494606
144	**12.** 820789688	1513	**5.** 875307972
1040	**13.** 291661724	765	**6.** 277997874
448	**14.** 230316784	493	**7.** 294492891
1344	**15.** 322121196	1445	**8.** 1450859718
640		697	**9.** 402573171
1536		1649	**10.** 417449571
832		901	**11.** 359898924
576	**No. 140**	153	**12.** 875472906
1472		1105	**13.** 311093013
768	17	476	**14.** 245661108
64	969	1428	**15.** 343581777
960	221	680	
256	1173	1632	
1152	425	884	**No. 148**
560	1377	912	
1456	629	1564	18
752	1581	816	1026
48	952	68	234
944	204	1020	1242
688	1156	272	450
1584	408	1224	1458
880	1360	595	666
176	136	1547	1674
1072	1088	799	1008

216	1080	247	760
1224	288	1311	1824
432	1296	475	988
1440	630	1539	684
144	1638	703	1748
1152	846	1767	912
360	54	1064	76
1368	1062	228	1140
576	774	1292	304
1584	1782	456	1368
792	990	1520	665
126	198	152	1729
1134	1206	1216	893
342	414	380	57
1350	1422	1444	1121
558	756	608	817
1566	1764	1672	1881
270	972	836	1045
1278	180	133	209
486	1188	1197	1273
1494	900	361	437
702	108	1425	1501
1710	1116	589	798
918	324	1653	1862
252	1332	285	1026
1260	540	1349	190
468	1548	513	1254
1476	882	1577	950
684	90	741	114
1692	1098	1805	1178
396	306	969	342
1404	1314	266	1406
612		1330	570
1620		494	1634
828	**No. 149**	1558	931
36		722	95
1044	**1.** 191239170	1786	1159
378	**2.** 191414406	418	323
1386	**3.** 208592688	1482	1387
594	**4.** 208767924	646	
1602	**5.** 929980808	1710	
810	**6.** 295361996	874	**No. 159**
522	**7.** 312887314	38	
1530	**8.** 1541482372	1102	**1.** 202481985
738	**9.** 427718434	399	**2.** 202667523
1746	**10.** 443524034	1463	**3.** 220855704
954	**11.** 382378696	627	**4.** 221041242
162	**12.** 930156124	1691	**5.** 984653804
1170	**13.** 330524302	855	**6.** 312726118
504	**14.** 261005432	551	**7.** 331281737
1512	**15.** 365042358	1615	**8.** 1632105026
720		779	**9.** 452863697
1728		1843	**10.** 469598497
936		1007	**11.** 404858468
648	**No. 156**	171	**12.** 984839342
1656		1235	**13.** 349955591
864	19	532	**14.** 276349756
72	1083	1596	**15.** 386502939

No. 165			
	180	**13.** 369386880	1785
	1300	**14.** 291694080	861
20	560	**15.** 407963520	2037
1140	1680		1113
260	800	No. 172	189
1380	1920		1365
500	1040	21	588
1620	720	1197	1744
740	1840	273	840
1860	960	1449	2016
1120	80	525	1092
240	1200	1701	756
1360	320	777	1932
480	1440	1953	1008
1600	700	1176	84
160	1820	252	1260
1280	940	1428	336
400	60	504	1512
1520	1180	1680	735
640	860	168	1911
1760	1980	1344	987
880	1100	420	63
140	220	1596	1239
1260	1340	672	903
380	460	1848	2079
1500	1580	924	1155
620	840	147	231
1740	1960	1323	1407
300	1080	399	483
1420	200	1575	1659
540	1320	651	882
1660	1000	1827	2058
780	120	315	1134
1900	1240	1491	210
1020	360	567	1386
280	1480	1743	1050
1400	600	819	126
520	1720	1995	1302
1640	980	1071	378
760	100	294	1554
1880	1220	1470	630
440	340	546	1806
1560	1460	1722	1029
680		798	105
1800	No. 166	1974	1281
920		462	357
40	**1.** 213724800	1638	1533
1160	**2.** 213920640	714	
420	**3.** 233118720	1890	
1540	**4.** 233314560	966	No. 173
660	**5.** 1039326720	42	
1780	**6.** 330090240	1218	**1.** 224967615
900	**7.** 349676160	441	**2.** 225173757
580	**8.** 1722727680	1617	**3.** 245381736
1700	**9.** 478008960	693	**4.** 245587878
820	**10.** 495672960	1869	**5.** 1093999636
1940	**11.** 427338240	945	**6.** 347454362
1060	**12.** 1039522560	609	**7.** 368070583

8. 1813350334	462	**2.** 236426874	506
9. 503154223	1694	**3.** 257644752	1794
10. 521747423	726	**4.** 257861196	782
11. 449818012	1958	**5.** 1148672552	2070
12. 1094205778	990	**6.** 364818484	1058
13. 388818169	638	**7.** 386465006	46
14. 307038404	1870	**8.** 1903972988	1334
15. 429424101	902	**9.** 528299486	483
	2134	**10.** 547821886	1771
	1166	**11.** 472297784	759
No. 179	198	**12.** 1148888996	2047
	1430	**13.** 408249458	1035
22	616	**14.** 322382728	667
1254	1848	**15.** 450884682	1955
286	880		943
1518	2112		2231
550	1144		1219
1782	792	**No. 186**	207
814	2024		1495
2046	1056	23	644
1232	88	1311	1932
264	1320	299	920
1496	352	1587	2208
528	1584	575	1196
1760	770	1863	828
176	2002	851	2116
1408	1034	2139	1104
440	66	1288	92
1672	1298	276	1380
704	946	1564	368
1936	2178	552	1656
968	1210	1840	805
154	242	184	2093
1386	1474	1472	1081
418	506	460	69
1650	1738	1748	1357
682	924	736	989
1914	2156	2024	2277
330	1188	1012	1265
1562	220	161	253
604	1452	1449	1541
1826	1100	437	529
858	132	1725	1817
2090	1364	713	966
1122	396	2001	2254
308	1628	345	1242
1540	660	1623	230
572	1892	621	1518
1804	1078	1909	1150
836	110	897	138
2068	1342	2185	1426
484	374	1173	414
1716	1606	322	1702
748		1610	690
1980		598	1978
1012	**No. 180**	1886	1127
44		874	115
1276	**1.** 236210430	2162	1403

391	336	1776	1775
1679	1680	720	675
	624	2064	2075
	1968	1176	975
No. 187	912	120	2375
	2256	1464	1275
1. 247453245	528	408	350
2. 247679991	1872	1752	1750
3. 269907768	816		650
4. 270134514	2160		2050
5. 1203345468	1104	**No. 194**	950
6. 382182606	48		2350
7. 404859429	1392	**1.** 258696060	550
8. 1994595642	504	**2.** 258933108	1950
9. 553444749	1848	**3.** 282170784	850
10. 573896349	792	**4.** 282407832	2250
11. 494777556	2136	**5.** 1258018384	1150
12. 1203572214	1080	**6.** 399546728	50
13. 427680747	696	**7.** 423253852	1450
14. 337727052	2040	**8.** 2085218296	525
15. 472345263	984	**9.** 578590012	1925
	2328	**10.** 599970812	825
	1272	**11.** 517257328	2225
No. 193	216	**12.** 1258255432	1125
	1560	**13.** 447112036	725
24	672	**14.** 353071376	2125
1368	2016	**15.** 493805844	1025
312	960		2425
1656	2304		1325
600	1248	**No. 200**	225
1944	864		1625
888	2208	25	700
2232	1152	1425	2100
1344	96	325	1000
288	1440	1725	2400
1632	384	625	1300
576	1728	2025	900
1920	840	925	2300
192	2184	2325	1200
1536	1128	1400	100
480	72	300	1500
1824	1416	1700	400
768	1032	600	1800
2112	2376	2000	875
1056	1320	200	2275
168	264	1600	1175
1512	1608	500	75
456	552	1900	1475
1800	1896	800	1075
744	1008	2200	2475
2088	2352	1100	1375
360	1296	175	275
1704	240	1575	1675
648	1584	475	575
1992	1200	1875	1975
936	144	775	1050
2280	1488	2175	2450
1224	432	375	1350

250
1650
1250
150
1550
450
1850
750
2150
1225
125
1525
425
1825

No. 201

1. 269938875
2. 270186225
3. 294433800
4. 294681150
5. 1312691300
6. 416910850
7. 441648275
3. 2175840950
9. 603735275
10. 626045275
11. 539737100
12. 1312938650
13. 466543325
14. 368415700
15. 515266425

No. 204

(*Annex 0 to Answers to No. 45*)

No. 208

(*Annex 0 to Answers to No. 46*)

No. 212

(*Annex 0 to Answers to No. 47*)

No. 215

(*Annex 0 to Answers to No. 50*)

No. 219

(*Annex 0 to Answers to No. 52*)

No. 222

(*Annex 0 to Answers to No. 53*)

No. 226

(*Annex 0 to Answers to No. 56*)

No. 228

(*Annex 0 to Answers to No. 60*)

No. 229

1. 242
2. 464
3. 686
4. 902
5. 1124
6. 1246
7. 1462
8. 1684
9. 1906
10. 322
11. 444
12. 666
13. 882
14. 1104
15. 1326
16. 1442
17. 1664
18. 1886
19. 302
20. 524

No. 232

(*Annex 0 to Answers to No. 61*)

No. 233

1. 393

2. 726
3. 1059
4. 1392
5. 1713
6. 1896
7. 2229
8. 2562
9. 2883
10. 516
11. 699
12. 1032
13. 1353
14. 1686
15. 2019
16. 2202
17. 2523
18. 2856
19. 489
20. 822

No. 236

(*Annex 0 to Answers to No. 77*)

No. 237

1. 564
2. 1008
3. 1452
4. 1896
5. 2340
6. 2564
7. 3008
8. 3452
9. 3892
10. 740
11. 964
12. 1408
13. 1852
14. 2296
15. 2740
16. 2964
17. 3408
18. 3852
19. 696
20. 1140

No. 239

(*Annex 0 to Answers to No. 90*)

No. 240

1. 755
2. 1310
3. 1865
4. 2420
5. 2975
6. 3280
7. 3805
8. 4360
9. 4915
10. 970
11. 1275
12. 1830
13. 2355
14. 2910
15. 3465
16. 3770
17. 4325
18. 4880
19. 905
20. 1460

No. 242

(*Annex 0 to Answers to No. 106*)

No. 243

1. 846
2. 1512
3. 2178
4. 2844
5. 3510
6. 4176
7. 4482
8. 5106
9. 5772
10. 1038
11. 1704
12. 2370
13. 2676
14. 3342
15. 3966
16. 4632
17. 5298
18. 5964
19. 870
20. 1536

No. 244

(*Annex 0 to Answers to No. 119*)

No. 245

1. 917
2. 1694
3. 2471
4. 3248
5. 4025
6. 4802
7. 5579
8. 5866
9. 6587
10. 1064
11. 1841
12. 2618
13. 3395
14. 4172
15. 4459
16. 5236
17. 5957
18. 6734
19. 1211
20. 1988

No. 246

(*Annex 0 to Answers to No. 131*)

No. 247

1. 1128
2. 2016
3. 2904
4. 3792
5. 4680
6. 5568
7. 5976
8. 6864
9. 7752
10. 1368
11. 2256
12. 3144
13. 3552
14. 4440
15. 5328
16. 6216
17. 7104
18. 7992
19. 5928
20. 5216

No. 248

1. $\frac{4}{8}$, $\frac{2}{8}$, $\frac{6}{8}$

2. $\frac{2}{16}$, $\frac{4}{16}$, $\frac{6}{16}$, $\frac{8}{16}$, $\frac{10}{16}$, $\frac{12}{16}$, $\frac{14}{16}$
3. $\frac{2}{6}$, $\frac{4}{6}$, $\frac{6}{6}$
4. $\frac{2}{12}$, $\frac{3}{12}$, $\frac{4}{12}$, $\frac{6}{12}$, $\frac{8}{12}$, $\frac{9}{12}$, $\frac{12}{12}$
5. $\frac{2}{24}$, $\frac{3}{24}$, $\frac{4}{24}$, $\frac{6}{24}$, $\frac{8}{24}$, $\frac{10}{24}$, $\frac{12}{24}$, $\frac{14}{24}$, $\frac{15}{24}$, $\frac{16}{24}$, $\frac{18}{24}$, $\frac{20}{24}$, $\frac{22}{24}$
6. $\frac{2}{10}$, $\frac{4}{10}$, $\frac{5}{10}$, $\frac{6}{10}$, $\frac{8}{10}$
7. $\frac{2}{20}$, $\frac{4}{20}$, $\frac{6}{20}$, $\frac{8}{20}$, $\frac{10}{20}$, $\frac{12}{20}$, $\frac{14}{20}$, $\frac{16}{20}$, $\frac{18}{20}$
8. $\frac{4}{40}$, $\frac{5}{40}$, $\frac{8}{40}$, $\frac{10}{40}$, $\frac{12}{40}$, $\frac{15}{40}$, $\frac{16}{40}$, $\frac{20}{40}$, $\frac{24}{40}$, $\frac{25}{40}$, $\frac{28}{40}$, $\frac{30}{40}$, $\frac{32}{40}$, $\frac{35}{40}$, $\frac{36}{40}$
9. $\frac{3}{15}$, $\frac{5}{15}$, $\frac{6}{15}$, $\frac{9}{15}$, $\frac{10}{15}$, $\frac{12}{15}$
10. $\frac{8}{30}$, $\frac{5}{30}$, $\frac{6}{30}$, $\frac{9}{30}$, $\frac{10}{30}$, $\frac{12}{30}$, $\frac{15}{30}$, $\frac{18}{30}$, $\frac{20}{30}$, $\frac{21}{30}$, $\frac{24}{30}$, $\frac{25}{30}$, $\frac{27}{30}$

No. 249

(*Annex 0 to Answers to No. 140*)

No. 250

1. $\frac{3}{4}$
2. $1\frac{1}{4}$
3. $\frac{5}{8}$
4. $\frac{7}{8}$
5. $1\frac{1}{8}$
6. $1\frac{3}{8}$
7. $\frac{3}{8}$
8. $\frac{5}{8}$
9. $\frac{7}{8}$
10. $1\frac{1}{8}$
11. $\frac{7}{8}$
12. $1\frac{1}{8}$
13. $1\frac{3}{8}$
14. $1\frac{5}{8}$
15. $\frac{9}{16}$
16. $\frac{11}{16}$
17. $\frac{13}{16}$
18. $\frac{15}{16}$

19. $1\frac{1}{16}$
20. $1\frac{3}{16}$
21. $1\frac{5}{16}$
22. $1\frac{7}{16}$
23. $\frac{5}{16}$
24. $\frac{7}{16}$
25. $\frac{9}{16}$
26. $\frac{11}{16}$
27. $\frac{13}{16}$
28. $\frac{15}{16}$
29. $1\frac{1}{16}$
30. $1\frac{3}{16}$
31. $\frac{13}{16}$
32. $\frac{15}{16}$
33. $1\frac{1}{16}$
34. $1\frac{3}{16}$
35. $1\frac{5}{16}$
36. $1\frac{7}{16}$
37. $1\frac{9}{16}$
38. $1\frac{11}{16}$
39. $\frac{3}{16}$
40. $\frac{5}{16}$

No. 251

1. 1368
2. 2367
3. 3366
4. 4365
5. 5364
6. 5823
7. 6822
8. 7821
9. 8757
10. 1656
11. 2655
12. 3114
13. 4113
14. 5112
15. 6111
16. 7056
17. 8055
18. 8514
19. 1413
20. 2412

No. 252

1. 121
2. 232
3. 343
4. 451
5. 562
6. 623
7. 731
8. 842

9. 953
10. 161
11. 222
12. 333
13. 441
14. 552
15. 663
16. 721
17. 832
18. 943
19. 151
20. 262

No. 253

1. $\frac{7}{16}$
2. $\frac{9}{10}$
3. $\frac{11}{16}$
4. $\frac{13}{16}$
5. $\frac{15}{16}$
6. $1\frac{1}{16}$
7. $\frac{7}{16}$
8. $\frac{9}{16}$
9. $\frac{11}{16}$
10. $\frac{13}{16}$

No. 254

(*Annex 0 to Answers to No. 148*)

No. 255

1. 131
2. 242
3. 353
4. 464
5. 571
6. 632
7. 743
8. 854
9. 961
10. 172
11. 233
12. 344
13. 451
14. 562
15. 673
16. 734
17. 841
18. 952
19. 163
20. 274

No. 256

1. $\frac{15}{16}$
2. $1\frac{1}{16}$
3. $1\frac{3}{16}$
4. $1\frac{5}{16}$
5. $1\frac{1}{16}$
6. $\frac{13}{16}$
7. $\frac{15}{16}$
8. $1\frac{1}{16}$
9. $1\frac{3}{16}$
10. $1\frac{5}{16}$

No. 257

(*Annex 0 to Answers to No. 156*)

No. 258

1. 141
2. 252
3. 363
4. 474
5. 585
6. 641
7. 752
8. 863
9. 974
10. 185
11. 241
12. 352
13. 463
14. 574
15. 685
16. 741
17. 852
18. 963
19. 174
20. 285

No. 259

1. $1\frac{7}{16}$
2. $1\frac{9}{16}$
3. $\frac{15}{16}$
4. $1\frac{1}{16}$
5. $1\frac{3}{16}$
6. $1\frac{5}{16}$
7. $1\frac{7}{16}$
8. $1\frac{9}{16}$
9. $1\frac{11}{16}$
10. $1\frac{3}{16}$

No. 260

(*Annex 0 to Answers to No. 165*)

No. 261

1. $\frac{1}{2}$
2. $\frac{5}{6}$
3. $\frac{5}{12}$
4. $\frac{3}{4}$
5. $1\frac{1}{2}$
6. $1\frac{1}{4}$
7. $\frac{3}{4}$
8. $1\frac{1}{2}$
9. $1\frac{1}{4}$
10. $1\frac{7}{12}$

No. 262

1. 151
2. 262
3. 373
4. 484
5. 595
6. 656
7. 761
8. 872
9. 983
10. 194
11. 255
12. 366
13. 471
14. 582
15. 693
16. 754
17. 865
18. 976
19. 181
20. 292

No. 263

1. $\frac{1}{4}$
2. $\frac{3}{4}$
3. $\frac{1}{8}$
4. $\frac{3}{8}$
5. $\frac{5}{8}$
6. $\frac{7}{8}$
7. $\frac{1}{8}$
8. $\frac{3}{8}$
9. $\frac{5}{8}$
10. $\frac{7}{8}$
11. $\frac{1}{8}$
12. $\frac{3}{8}$
13. $\frac{5}{8}$
14. $\frac{7}{8}$
15. $\frac{1}{16}$
16. $\frac{3}{16}$
17. $\frac{5}{16}$
18. $\frac{7}{16}$
19. $\frac{9}{16}$
20. $\frac{11}{16}$
21. $\frac{13}{16}$
22. $\frac{15}{16}$
23. $\frac{1}{16}$
24. $\frac{3}{16}$
25. $\frac{5}{16}$
26. $\frac{7}{16}$
27. $\frac{9}{16}$
28. $\frac{11}{16}$
29. $\frac{13}{16}$
30. $\frac{15}{16}$

No. 264

(*Annex 0 to Answers to No. 172*)

No. 265

1. $\frac{1}{16}$
2. $\frac{3}{16}$
3. $\frac{5}{16}$
4. $\frac{7}{16}$
5. $\frac{9}{16}$
6. $\frac{11}{16}$
7. $\frac{13}{16}$
8. $\frac{15}{16}$
9. $\frac{1}{16}$
10. $\frac{3}{16}$

No. 266

1. 141
2. 252
3. 363
4. 474
5. 585
6. 696
7. 747
8. 851
9. 962
10. 173
11. 284
12. 395
13. 446
14. 557
15. 661
16. 772
17. 883
18. 994
19. 145
20. 256

No. 267

1. $\frac{1}{4}$
2. $\frac{7}{12}$
3. $\frac{3}{4}$
4. $1\frac{1}{12}$
5. $1\frac{1}{3}$
6. $1\frac{1}{4}$
7. $1\frac{5}{12}$
8. $1\frac{3}{4}$
9. $\frac{5}{6}$
10. $1\frac{1}{6}$

No. 268

(*Annex 0 to Answers to No. 179*)

No. 269

1. $\frac{5}{16}$
2. $\frac{7}{16}$
3. $\frac{9}{16}$
4. $\frac{11}{16}$
5. $\frac{13}{16}$
6. $\frac{15}{16}$
7. $\frac{1}{16}$
8. $\frac{3}{16}$
9. $\frac{5}{16}$
10. $\frac{7}{16}$

No. 270

1. 131
2. 242
3. 353
4. 464
5. 575
6. 686
7. 797
8. 838
9. 941
10. 152
11. 263
12. 374
13. 485

14. 596
15. 637
16. 748
17. 851
18. 962
19. 173
20. 284

No. 271

1. $\frac{2}{3}$
2. $1\frac{1}{3}$
3. $\frac{5}{12}$
4. $1\frac{1}{12}$
5. $1\frac{1}{12}$
6. $1\frac{7}{12}$
7. $\frac{7}{24}$
8. $\frac{13}{24}$
9. $\frac{19}{24}$
10. $1\frac{9}{24}$

No. 272

(Annex 0 to Answers to No. 186)

No. 273

1. $\frac{9}{16}$
2. $\frac{11}{16}$
3. $\frac{13}{16}$
4. $\frac{15}{16}$
5. $\frac{1}{16}$
6. $\frac{3}{16}$
7. $\frac{5}{16}$
8. $\frac{7}{16}$
9. $\frac{9}{16}$
10. $\frac{11}{16}$

No. 274

1. 141
2. 252
3. 363
4. 474
5. 585
6. 696
7. 747
8. 858
9. 969
10. 171
11. 282

12. 393
13. 444
14. 555
15. 666
16. 777
17. 888
18. 999
19. 741
20. 652

No. 275

1. $\frac{23}{24}$
2. $1\frac{5}{24}$
3. $1\frac{11}{24}$
4. $1\frac{17}{24}$
5. $\frac{7}{12}$
6. $\frac{11}{12}$
7. $1\frac{1}{12}$
8. $1\frac{5}{12}$
9. $\frac{1}{3}$
10. $\frac{2}{3}$

No. 276

(Annex 0 to Answers to No. 193)

No. 277

1. $\frac{13}{16}$
2. $\frac{15}{16}$
3. $\frac{1}{16}$
4. $\frac{3}{16}$
5. $\frac{5}{16}$
6. $\frac{7}{16}$
7. $\frac{9}{16}$
8. $\frac{11}{16}$
9. $\frac{13}{16}$
10. $\frac{15}{16}$

No. 278

1. 152
2. 263
3. 374
4. 485
5. 596
6. 647
7. 758

8. 869
9. 973
10. 184
11. 295
12. 346
13. 437
14. 568
15. 679
16. 784
17. 895
18. 946
19. 157
20. 268

No. 279

1. $\frac{5}{8}$
2. $1\frac{1}{6}$
3. $\frac{5}{8}$
4. $1\frac{1}{6}$
5. $1\frac{1}{3}$
6. $1\frac{2}{3}$
7. $\frac{5}{24}$
8. $\frac{13}{24}$
9. $\frac{17}{24}$
10. $1\frac{1}{24}$

No. 280

(Annex 0 to Answers to No. 200)

No. 281

1. $\frac{1}{6}$
2. $\frac{1}{6}$
3. $\frac{1}{12}$
4. $\frac{5}{12}$
5. $\frac{7}{12}$
6. $\frac{11}{12}$
7. $\frac{1}{12}$
8. $\frac{5}{12}$
9. $\frac{7}{12}$
10. $\frac{11}{12}$

No. 282

1. 2r86
2. 2r129
3. 2r108
4. 2r347
5. 2r456
6. 2r589

7. 2r312
8. 2r102
9. 2r208
10. 2r117
11. 3r13
12. 3r50
13. 3r105
14. 3r182
15. 3r285
16. 4r126
17. 4r200
18. 4r252
19. 4r282
20. 4r280

No. 283

1. $\frac{11}{24}$
2. $\frac{19}{24}$
3. $\frac{23}{24}$
4. $1\frac{7}{24}$
5. $1\frac{11}{24}$
6. $1\frac{1}{24}$
7. $1\frac{5}{24}$
8. $1\frac{13}{24}$
9. $\frac{23}{24}$
10. $1\frac{7}{24}$

No. 284

1. 1066
2. 1377
3. 1708
4. 2059
5. 2511
6. 2912
7. 1023
8. 1394
9. 1326
10. 1647
11. 1988
12. 2349
13. 2821
14. 992
15. 1353
16. 1734
17. 1586
18. 1917
19. 2268
20. 2639

No. 285

1. $\frac{1}{12}$
2. $\frac{5}{12}$
3. $\frac{7}{12}$

4. $\frac{11}{12}$
5. $\frac{1}{12}$
6. $\frac{5}{12}$
7. $\frac{7}{12}$
8. $1\frac{1}{12}$
9. $\frac{2}{3}$
10. $\frac{2}{3}$

No. 286

1. 2r1
2. 2r29
3. 2r376
4. 2r551
5. 2r374
6. 3r378
7. 3r518
8. 3r680
9. 3r864
10. 3r17
11. 4r266
12. 4r225
13. 4r172
14. 4r93
15. 4r162
16. 5r90
17. 5r130
18. 5r148
19. 5r144
20. 5r119

No. 287

1. $1\frac{11}{24}$
2. $1\frac{19}{24}$
3. $\frac{3}{16}$
4. $\frac{1}{2}$
5. $\frac{9}{10}$
6. $1\frac{1}{10}$
7. $\frac{1}{2}$
8. $\frac{7}{10}$
9. $1\frac{1}{10}$
10. $1\frac{3}{10}$

No. 288

1. 1470
2. 1872
3. 2294
4. 2736
5. 3198
6. 3772
7. 1344
8. 1806
9. 1820
10. 2232
11. 2664
12. 3116
13. 3588
14. 1312
15. 1764
16. 2236
17. 2108
18. 2520
19. 2952
20. 3404

No. 289

1. $\frac{1}{6}$
2. $\frac{5}{6}$
3. $\frac{5}{6}$
4. $\frac{9}{24}$
5. $\frac{5}{6}$
6. $\frac{5}{6}$
7. $\frac{1}{6}$
8. $\frac{1}{6}$
9. $\frac{1}{6}$
10. $\frac{1}{6}$

No. 290

1. 2r37
2. 2r771
3. 2r150
4. 2r85
5. 2r99
6. 3r46
7. 3r102
8. 3r170
9. 3r280
10. 3r402
11. 4r192
12. 4r235
13. 4r276
14. 4r285
15. 4r272
16. 5r67
17. 5r693
18. 5r564
19. 5r632
20. 5r97

No. 291

1. $\frac{7}{10}$
2. $\frac{9}{10}$
3. $1\frac{3}{10}$
4. $1\frac{1}{2}$
5. $\frac{9}{10}$
6. $1\frac{1}{10}$
7. $1\frac{1}{2}$
8. $1\frac{7}{10}$
9. $\frac{7}{10}$
10. $\frac{9}{10}$

No. 292

1. 1892
2. 2385
3. 2898
4. 3431
5. 3984
6. 4557
7. 1683
8. 2236
9. 2332
10. 2835
11. 3358
12. 3901
13. 4464
14. 1617
15. 2193
16. 2756
17. 2772
18. 3510
19. 3818
20. 4371

No. 293

1. $\frac{5}{6}$
2. $\frac{5}{6}$
3. $\frac{5}{6}$
4. $\frac{5}{6}$
5. $\frac{1}{12}$
6. $\frac{5}{12}$
7. $\frac{7}{12}$
8. $\frac{11}{12}$
9. $\frac{1}{12}$
10. $\frac{5}{12}$

No. 294

1. 3r51
2. 3r69
3. 3r95
4. 3r32
5. 3r54
6. 4r226
7. 4r85
8. 4r864
9. 4r119
10. 4r208
11. 5r146
12. 5r288
13. 5r321
14. 5r465
15. 5r108
16. 6r125
17. 6r200
18. 6r77
19. 6r111
20. 6r310

No. 295

1. $1\frac{1}{10}$
2. $1\frac{3}{10}$
3. $\frac{3}{5}$
4. $\frac{4}{5}$
5. $1\frac{1}{5}$
6. $1\frac{2}{5}$
7. $\frac{9}{20}$
8. $\frac{3}{20}$
9. $\frac{17}{20}$
10. $1\frac{1}{20}$

No. 296

1. 2332
2. 2916
3. 3520
4. 4144
5. 4788
6. 5452
7. 2006
8. 2684
9. 2862
10. 3456
11. 4070
12. 4704
14. 1972
15. 2596
16. 3599
17. 3392
18. 3996
19. 4620
20. 5264

No. 297

1. $\frac{7}{12}$
2. $\frac{11}{12}$
3. $\frac{1}{12}$
4. $\frac{6}{12}$

5. $\frac{7}{12}$
6. $\frac{11}{12}$
7. $\frac{1}{12}$
8. $\frac{5}{12}$
9. $\frac{7}{12}$
10. $\frac{11}{12}$

No. 298

1. 5r219
2. 5r642
3. 5r312
4. 5r97
5. 5r106
6. 6r310
7. 6r150
8. 6r100
9. 6r609
10. 6r115
11. 7r65
12. 7r135
13. 7r235
14. 7r185
15. 7r64
16. 8r72
17. 8r125
18. 8r180
19. 8r360
20. 8r421

No. 299

1. $\frac{7}{20}$
2. $\frac{11}{20}$
3. $\frac{19}{20}$
4. $1\frac{3}{20}$
5. $\frac{19}{20}$
6. $1\frac{3}{20}$
7. $1\frac{7}{20}$
8. $1\frac{11}{20}$
9. $\frac{17}{20}$
10. $1\frac{1}{20}$

No. 300

1. 2790
2. 3465
3. 4160
4. 4875
5. 5610
6. 6365
7. 2380
8. 3105

9. 3410
10. 4095
11. 4800
12. 5525
13. 6270
14. 2345
15. 3060
16. 3795
17. 4030
18. 4725
19. 5440
20. 6175

No. 301

1. $\frac{1}{12}$
2. $\frac{5}{12}$
3. $\frac{7}{12}$
4. $\frac{11}{12}$
5. $\frac{1}{12}$
6. $\frac{5}{12}$
7. $\frac{7}{12}$
8. $\frac{11}{12}$
9. $\frac{1}{12}$
10. $\frac{5}{12}$

No. 302

1. 6r10
2. 6r29
3. 6r38
4. 6r165
5. 6r651
6. 7r501
7. 7r307
8. 7r799
9. 7r646
10. 7r20
11. 8r189
12. 8r612
13. 8r325
14. 8r486
15. 8r17
16. 9r125
17. 9r135
18. 9r74
19. 9r85
20. 9r59

No. 303

1. $1\frac{9}{20}$
2. $1\frac{13}{20}$
3. $1\frac{13}{40}$
4. $\frac{21}{40}$

5. $\frac{23}{40}$
6. $\frac{27}{40}$
7. $\frac{9}{40}$
8. $\frac{17}{40}$
9. $\frac{33}{40}$
10. $1\frac{1}{40}$

No. 304

1. 3266
2. 4032
3. 4818
4. 5624
5. 6450
6. 7296
7. 2772
8. 3588
9. 3976
10. 4752
11. 5548
12. 6364
13. 7200
14. 2736
15. 3542
16. 4368
17. 4686
18. 5472
19. 6278
20. 7104

No. 305

1. $\frac{7}{12}$
2. $\frac{11}{12}$
3. $\frac{3}{10}$
4. $\frac{8}{10}$
5. $\frac{7}{10}$
6. $\frac{9}{10}$
7. $\frac{1}{10}$
8. $\frac{8}{10}$
9. $\frac{7}{10}$
10. $\frac{9}{10}$

No. 306

1. 6r706
2. 6r95
3. 6r37
4. 6r38
5. 6r40
6 7r18
7. 7r118
8. 7r211
9. 7r346
10. 7r252
11. 8r28
12. 8r39

13. 8r404
14. 8r355
15. 8r626
16. 9r64
17. 9r301
18. 9r400
19. 9r500
20. 9r65

No. 307

1. $\frac{23}{40}$
2. $\frac{31}{40}$
3. $\frac{39}{40}$
4. $1\frac{7}{40}$
5. $\frac{19}{40}$
6. $\frac{27}{40}$
7. $1\frac{3}{40}$
8. $1\frac{11}{40}$
9. $\frac{33}{40}$
10. $1\frac{7}{40}$

No. 308

1. 3713
2. 4617
3. 5494
4. 6391
5. 7308
6. 8245
7. 3182
8. 4089
9. 4503
10. 5427
11. 6314
12. 7221
13. 8148
14. 3145
15. 4042
16. 4959
17. 5293
18. 6237
19. 7134
20. 8051

No. 309

1. $\frac{1}{10}$
2. $\frac{8}{10}$
3. $\frac{7}{10}$
4. $\frac{9}{10}$
5. $\frac{7}{10}$
6. $\frac{8}{10}$
7. $\frac{7}{10}$
8. $\frac{9}{10}$

9. $\frac{1}{5}$
10. $\frac{2}{5}$

No. 310

1. 7r129
2. 7r642
3. 7r711
4. 7r32
5. 7r232
6. 8r77
7. 8r444
8. 8r312
9. 8r147
10. 8r25
11. 9r27
12. 9r297
13. 9r358
14. 9r555
15. 9r609
16. 9r775
17. 9r862
18. 9r927
19. 9r150
20. 9r215

No. 311

1. $1\frac{9}{40}$
2. $1\frac{17}{40}$
3. $\frac{29}{40}$
4. $\frac{37}{40}$
5. $1\frac{3}{40}$
6. $1\frac{21}{40}$
7. $1\frac{3}{40}$
8. $1\frac{11}{40}$
9. $1\frac{19}{40}$
10. $1\frac{27}{40}$

No. 312

1. 4224
2. 5162
3. 6188
4. 7176
5. 8184
6. 9212
7. 3610
8. 4608
9. 5104
10. 6052
11. 7098
12. 8096
13. 9114
14. 3572

15. 4560
16. 5568
17. 5984
18. 6942
19. 8008
20. 9016

No. 313

1. $\frac{8}{5}$
2. $\frac{4}{5}$
3. $\frac{1}{10}$
4. $\frac{3}{10}$
5. $\frac{7}{10}$
6. $\frac{1}{10}$
7. $\frac{1}{5}$
8. $\frac{2}{5}$
9. $\frac{3}{5}$
10. $\frac{4}{5}$

No. 314

1. $\frac{38}{40}$
2. $1\frac{7}{40}$
3. $1\frac{28}{40}$
4. $1\frac{11}{15}$
5. $\frac{8}{15}$
6. $1\frac{1}{15}$
7. $1\frac{4}{15}$
8. $1\frac{2}{15}$
9. $1\frac{13}{30}$
10. $1\frac{18}{30}$

No. 315

1. 4655
2. 5664
3. 6693
4. 7742
5. 8811
6. 9405
7. 3744
8. 4753
9. 5782
10. 6831
11. 7505
12. 8544
13. 9603
14. 3822
15. 4851
16. 5605
17. 6624
18. 7663
19. 8722
20. 9801

No. 316

1. $\frac{1}{10}$
2. $\frac{3}{10}$
3. $\frac{7}{10}$
4. $\frac{9}{10}$
5. $\frac{1}{5}$
6. $\frac{2}{5}$
7. $\frac{3}{5}$
8. $\frac{4}{5}$
9. $\frac{1}{10}$
10. $\frac{3}{10}$

No. 317

1. $1\frac{1}{30}$
2. $1\frac{7}{30}$
3. $1\frac{13}{15}$
4. $1\frac{1}{15}$
5. $1\frac{4}{15}$
6. $1\frac{7}{15}$
7. $2\frac{8}{30}$
8. $2\frac{9}{30}$
9. $1\frac{11}{30}$
10. $1\frac{17}{30}$

No. 318

1. $\frac{7}{10}$
2. $\frac{9}{10}$
3. $\frac{1}{5}$
4. $\frac{2}{5}$
5. $\frac{3}{5}$
6. $\frac{4}{5}$
7. $\frac{7}{10}$
8. $\frac{8}{10}$
9. $\frac{7}{10}$
10. $\frac{9}{10}$

No. 319

1. 41
2. 51
3. 61
4. 71
5. 81
6. 91
7. 31
8. 41
9. 51
10. 61
11. 71
12. 81
13. 91

14. 31
15. 41
16. 51
17. 61
18. 71
19. 81
20. 91

No. 320

1. $\frac{11}{30}$
2. $\frac{17}{30}$
3. $\frac{23}{30}$
4. $\frac{29}{30}$
5. $\frac{4}{15}$
6. $\frac{7}{15}$
7. $\frac{13}{15}$
8. $1\frac{1}{15}$
9. $1\frac{1}{30}$
10. $1\frac{7}{30}$

No. 321

1. $\frac{1}{8}$
2. $\frac{3}{8}$
3. $\frac{5}{8}$
4. $\frac{4}{5}$
5. $\frac{1}{10}$
6. $\frac{3}{10}$
7. $\frac{7}{10}$
8. $\frac{9}{10}$
9. $\frac{4}{5}$
10. $\frac{2}{5}$

No. 322

1. 42
2. 52
3. 62
4. 72
5. 82
6. 92
7. 32
8. 42
9. 52
10. 62
11. 72
12. 82
13. 92
14. 32
15. 42
16. 52
17. 62
18. 72
19. 82

20. 92

No. 323
1. $1\frac{13}{30}$
2. $1\frac{19}{30}$
3. $1\frac{4}{15}$
4. $1\frac{2}{15}$
5. $1\frac{8}{15}$
6. $1\frac{11}{15}$

No. 324
1. $\frac{3}{5}$
2. $\frac{4}{5}$
3. $\frac{1}{10}$
4. $\frac{3}{10}$
5. $\frac{7}{10}$
6. $\frac{9}{10}$
7. $\frac{1}{5}$
8. $\frac{2}{5}$
9. $\frac{3}{5}$
10. $\frac{4}{5}$

No. 325
1. 43
2. 53
3. 63
4. 73
5. 83
6. 93
7. 33
8. 43
9. 53
10. 63
11. 73
12. 83
13. 93
14. 33
15. 43
16. 53
17. 63
18. 73
19. 83
20. 93

No. 327
1. $\frac{1}{10}$
2. $\frac{3}{10}$
3. $\frac{7}{10}$
4. $\frac{9}{10}$
5. $\frac{1}{5}$

6. $\frac{2}{3}$
7. $\frac{3}{5}$
8. $\frac{4}{5}$
9. $\frac{1}{10}$
10. $\frac{3}{10}$

No. 328
1. 44
2. 54
3. 64
4. 74
5. 84
6. 94
7. 34
8. 44
9. 54
10. 64
11. 74
12. 84
13. 94
14. 34
15. 44
16. 54
17. 64
18. 74
19. 84
20. 94

No. 330
1. $\frac{7}{10}$
2. $\frac{9}{10}$
3. $\frac{1}{5}$
4. $\frac{3}{5}$
5. $\frac{3}{5}$
6. $\frac{4}{5}$
7. $\frac{1}{10}$
8. $\frac{3}{10}$
9. $\frac{7}{10}$
10. $\frac{9}{10}$

No. 331
1. 45
2. 55
3. 65
4. 75
5. 85
6. 95
7. 35
8. 45
9. 55
10. 65
11. 75
12. 85

13. 95
14. 35
15. 45
16. 55
17. 65
18. 75
19. 85
20. 95

No. 332
1. 46
2. 56
3. 66
4. 76
5. 86
6. 96
7. 36
8. 46
9. 56
10. 66
11. 76
12. 86
13. 96
14. 36
15. 46
16. 56
17. 66
18. 76
19. 86
20. 96

No. 333
1. $\frac{1}{5}$
2. $\frac{2}{5}$
3. $\frac{3}{5}$
4. $\frac{4}{5}$
5. $\frac{1}{10}$
6. $\frac{3}{10}$
7. $\frac{7}{10}$
8. $\frac{1}{5}$
9. $\frac{1}{5}$
10. $\frac{2}{5}$

No. 334
1. 47
2. 57
3. 67
4. 77
5. 87
6. 97
7. 37
8. 47
9. 57

10. 67
11. 77
12. 87
13. 97
14. 37
15. 47
16. 57
17. 67
18. 77
19. 87
20. 97

No. 335
1. $\frac{3}{5}$
2. $\frac{4}{5}$
3. $\frac{1}{10}$
4. $\frac{3}{10}$
5. $\frac{7}{10}$
6. $\frac{9}{10}$

No. 336
1. 48
2. 58
3. 68
4. 78
5. 88
6. 98
7. 38
8. 48
9. 58
10. 68
11. 78
12. 88
13. 98
14. 38
15. 48
16. 58
17. 68
18. 78
19. 88
20. 98

No. 337
1. 49
2. 59
3. 69
4. 79
5. 89
6. 99
7. 39
8. 49
9. 59
10. 69

11. 79
12. 89
13. 99
14. 39
15. 49
16. 59
17. 69
18. 79
19. 89
20. 99

No. 338

1. .12$\frac{1}{2}$
2. .37$\frac{1}{2}$
3. .62$\frac{1}{2}$
4. .87$\frac{1}{2}$
5. .33$\frac{1}{3}$
6. .66$\frac{2}{3}$
7. .16$\frac{2}{3}$
8. .83$\frac{1}{3}$
9. .20
10. .40
11. .60
12. .80

No. 339

1. 2886
2. 5994
3. 9268
4. 12818
5. 17081
6. 19584
7. 23793
8. 28288
9. 24466
10. 4104

No. 340

1. .06$\frac{1}{4}$
2. .18$\frac{3}{4}$
3. .31$\frac{1}{4}$
4. .43$\frac{3}{4}$
5. .56$\frac{1}{4}$
6. .68$\frac{3}{4}$
7. .81$\frac{1}{4}$
8. .93$\frac{3}{4}$
9. .08$\frac{1}{3}$
10. .41$\frac{2}{3}$
11. .58$\frac{1}{3}$
12. .91$\frac{2}{3}$
13. .03$\frac{1}{8}$
14. .04$\frac{1}{6}$

No. 341

1. 4235
2. 8352
3. 12691
4. 17138
5. 21918
6. 25543
7. 30702
8. 36206
9. 33355
10. 5796

No. 342

1. $17887
2. $9818
3. 9865
4. 25775
5. 39540
6. 23332
7. 17313
8. 31383
9. $14822.40
10. 243062

No. 343

1. 5764
2. 10890
3. 16238
4. 21808
5. 27408
6. 30968
7. 37893
8. 44408
9. 42284
10. 7740

No. 344

1. .0625
2. .1875
3. .3125
4. .4375
5. .5625
6. .6875
7. .8125
8. .9375
9. .0833$\frac{1}{3}$
10. .4166$\frac{2}{3}$
11. .5833$\frac{1}{3}$
12. .9166$\frac{2}{3}$
13. .0312$\frac{1}{2}$
14. .0416$\frac{2}{3}$

No. 345

1. 7473
2. 13608
3. 19965
4. 26544
5. 33345
6. 37178
7. 44368
8. 52643
9. 51622
10. 9990

No. 346

1. $99.84
2. 96256
3. $117.76
4. 98304
5. 1728
6. $675.84
7. $8120.60
8. $30402.55

No. 347

1. 9362
2. 16506
3. 23872
4. 31460
5. 39270
6. 43952
7. 51748
8. 60168
9. 60946
10. 12222

No. 348

1. .03125
2. .09375
3. .15625
4. .21875
5. .28125
6. .34375
7. .40625
8. .46875
9. .53125
10. .59375
11. .65625
12. .71875
13. .78125
14. .84375
15. .90625
16. .96875
17. .04167
18. .20833
19. .29167
20. .45833
21. .54167
22. .70833
23. .79167
24. .95833

No. 349

1. 10011
2. 18144
3. 26499
4. 35076
5. 43875
6. 52896
7. 57519
8. 66378
9. 68302
10. 12456

No. 350

1. $424575
2. $84770
3. $733779.50
4. $26863.20
5. $830062.74
6. $526.32
7. $981088
8. $9603
9. $1007010

No. 351

1. 10349
2. 19602
3. 28946
4. 38512
5. 48300
6. 58310
7. 68542
8. 72906
9. 74339
10. 12312

No. 353

1. 12408
2. 22428
3. 33033
4. 43608
5. 54405
6. 65424

7. 70965
8. 82368
9. 85272
10. 15219

No. 354

1. $525
2. $756
3. $384
4. $810
5. $5400
6. $900
7. $13000
8. $14700
9. $7200
10. $1600
11. $630
12. $12600
13. $1200
14. $1200
15. $1200

No. 355

1. 14440
2. 25248
3. 36278
4. 47530
5. 59004
6. 61465
7. 72768
8. 84293
9. 95354
10. 192 06

No. 357

1. 11211
2. 24642
3. 40051
4. 57902
5. 77691
6. 92412
7. 116081
8. 142272
9. 170321
10. 29032

No. 358

1. $247715.70
2. $243540
3. $60226335
4. $1087638.75

5. $5209451.52
6. $131602.24
7. $40102686.72
8. $8710669

No. 359

1. 24442
2. 49184
3. 76146
4. 104632
5. 136004
6. 156996
7. 191522
8. 229024
9. 268746
10. 47012

No. 361

1. 39693
2. 75746
3. 114019
4. 154512
5. 195853
6. 223096
7. 269709
8. 318542
9. 368063
10. 67596

No. 362

1. 138138
2. 115596
3. 74556
4. 186960
5. 89301
6. 235872
7. 119782
8. 73248
9. 193256

No. 363

1. 56964
2. 104328
3. 153912
4. 205716
5. 259740
6. 291014
7. 348928
8. 409062
9. 471416
10. 91390

No. 364

1. 210
2. 342
3. 255
4. 240
5. 195
6. 247
7. 272
8. 224
9. 361

No. 365

1. 76255
2. 134930
3. 195825
4. 258940
5. 324275
6. 364080
7. 429965
8. 501400
9. 575055
10. 115430

No. 366

1. $56496
2. $799018
3. $5663152
4. $410091.55
5. $453952.95
6. $36033.25
7. $530895.75
8. $1043606.30

No. 367

1. 85446
2. 155232
3. 227238
4. 301464
5. 377910
6. 456576
7. 497502
8. 575276
9. 659932
10. 120408

No. 368

1. $139510.50

2. $147804.75
3. $158233.30
4. $131011.65
5. $452339.40
6. $754503.75
7. $151524.65
8. $238939.80

No. 369

1. 92617
2. 173514
3. 256631
4. 341968
5. 429525
6. 519302
7. 611299
8. 651126
9. 740567
10. 121144

No. 370

1. 5476
2. 8649
3. 6724
4. 4096
5. 1444
6. 12544
7. 15376
8. 21316
9. 28224
10. 38809
11. 1236544
12. 1471369
13. 1726596
14. 2298256
15. 2954961

No. 371

1. 113928
2. 206136
3. 300564
4. 397212
5. 496080
6. 597168
7. 648396
8. 753324
9. 860472
10. 153558

No. 372

1. 7616

2. 12561
3. 15824
4. 22425
5. 40716
6. 42749
7. 421056
8. 224196
9. 198989

No. 373

1. 138168
2. 241697
3. 347446
4. 455415
5. 565604
6. 620473
7. 734502
8. 850751
9. 962297
10. 183816

No. 374

1. 8556
2. 4030
3. 7308
4. 8924
5. 45795
6. 100152
7. 173888
8. 264171
9. 837221

No. 375

1. 2025
2. 3025

3. 4225
4. 5625
5. 7225
6. 9025
7. 13225
8. 18225
9. 24025
10. 30625
11. 38025
12. 99225
13. 112225
14. 126025
15. 140625

No. 376

1. 621
2. 2009
3. 1224
4. 11021
5. 13216
6. 24024
7. 30616
8. 27209
9. 38016

No. 377

1. 275625
2. 390625
3. 680625
4. 1050625
5. 1500625
6. 1755625
7. 2640625
8. 2975625

9. 3330625
10. 3705625

No. 378

1. 4896
2. 6391
3. 8084
4. 12019
5. 16851
6. 22484
7. 25536
8. 32351
9. 36036

No. 379

1. $90\frac{2}{3}$
2. $112\frac{9}{25}$
3. $160\frac{5}{12}$
4. $339\frac{1}{6}$
5. $12\frac{2}{9}$
6. $3681\frac{9}{70}$
7. $1625\frac{3}{32}$
8. $650\frac{9}{25}$
9. $28\frac{7}{8}$
10. $72\frac{11}{12}$
11. $42\frac{15}{64}$
12. $152\frac{5}{81}$

No. 380

1. 276
2. 800
3. $929\frac{1}{3}$
4. 950

5. 2552
6. 5952
7. 1422
8. 2100
9. 3363

No. 381

1. 23.2
2. 45
3. 36
4. 3.5
5. 5.12
6. 13.05
7. 10.18
8. 61.2
9. 77.6

No. 382

1. 2744
2. 19683
3. 35937
4. 97336
5. 205379
6. 238328
7. 274625
8. 357911
9. 389017
10. 592704
11. 636056
12. 681472
13. 857375
14. 912673
15. 970299

CATALOGUE OF DOVER BOOKS

Books Explaining Science and Mathematics

WHAT IS SCIENCE?, N. Campbell. The role of experiment and measurement, the function of mathematics, the nature of scientific laws, the difference between laws and theories, the limitations of science, and many similarly provocative topics are treated clearly and without technicalities by an eminent scientist. "Still an excellent introduction to scientific philosophy," H. Margenau in PHYSICS TODAY. "A first-rate primer . . . deserves a wide audience," SCIENTIFIC AMERICAN. 192pp. 5⅜ x 8.   S43 Paperbound **$1.25**

THE NATURE OF PHYSICAL THEORY, P. W. Bridgman. A Nobel Laureate's clear, non-technical lectures on difficulties and paradoxes connected with frontier research on the physical sciences. Concerned with such central concepts as thought, logic, mathematics, relativity, probability, wave mechanics, etc. he analyzes the contributions of such men as Newton, Einstein, Bohr, Heisenberg, and many others. "Lucid and entertaining . . . recommended to anyone who wants to get some insight into current philosophies of science," THE NEW PHILOSOPHY. Index. xi + 138pp. 5⅜ x 8.   S33 Paperbound **$1.25**

EXPERIMENT AND THEORY IN PHYSICS, Max Born. A Nobel Laureate examines the nature of experiment and theory in theoretical physics and analyzes the advances made by the great physicists of our day: Heisenberg, Einstein, Bohr, Planck, Dirac, and others. The actual process of creation is detailed step-by-step by one who participated. A fine examination of the scientific method at work. 44pp. 5⅜ x 8.   S308 Paperbound **75¢**

THE PSYCHOLOGY OF INVENTION IN THE MATHEMATICAL FIELD, J. Hadamard. The reports of such men as Descartes, Pascal, Einstein, Poincaré, and others are considered in this investigation of the method of idea-creation in mathematics and other sciences and the thinking process in general. How do ideas originate? What is the role of the unconscious? What is Poincaré's forgetting hypothesis? are some of the fascinating questions treated. A penetrating analysis of Einstein's thought processes concludes the book. xiii + 145pp. 5⅜ x 8.   T107 Paperbound **$1.25**

THE NATURE OF LIGHT AND COLOUR IN THE OPEN AIR, M. Minnaert. Why are shadows sometimes blue, sometimes green, or other colors depending on the light and surroundings? What causes mirages? Why do multiple suns and moons appear in the sky? Professor Minnaert explains these unusual phenomena and hundreds of others in simple, easy-to-understand terms based on optical laws and the properties of light and color. No mathematics is required but artists, scientists, students, and everyone fascinated by these "tricks" of nature will find thousands of useful and amazing pieces of information. Hundreds of observational experiments are suggested which require no special equipment. 200 illustrations; 42 photos. xvi + 362pp. 5⅜ x 8.   T196 Paperbound **$2.00**

THE UNIVERSE OF LIGHT, W. Bragg. Sir William Bragg, Nobel Laureate and great modern physicist, is also well known for his powers of clear exposition. Here he analyzes all aspects of light for the layman: lenses, reflection, refraction, the optics of vision, x-rays, the photoelectric effect, etc. He tells you what causes the color of spectra, rainbows, and soap bubbles, how magic mirrors work, and much more. Dozens of simple experiments are described. Preface. Index. 199 line drawings and photographs, including 2 full-page color plates. x + 283pp. 5⅜ x 8.   T538 Paperbound **$1.85**

SOAP-BUBBLES: THEIR COLOURS AND THE FORCES THAT MOULD THEM, C. V. Boys. For continuing popularity and validity as scientific primer, few books can match this volume of easily-followed experiments, explanations. Lucid exposition of complexities of liquid films, surface tension and related phenomena, bubbles' reaction to heat, motion, music, magnetic fields. Experiments with capillary attraction, soap bubbles on frames, composite bubbles, liquid cylinders and jets, bubbles other than soap, etc. Wonderful introduction to scientific method, natural laws that have many ramifications in areas of modern physics. Only complete edition in print. New Introduction by S. Z. Lewin, New York University. 83 illustrations; 1 full-page color plate. xii + 190pp. 5⅜ x 8½.   T542 Paperbound **95¢**

THE STORY OF X-RAYS FROM RONTGEN TO ISOTOPES, A. R. Bleich, M.D. This book, by a member of the American College of Radiology, gives the scientific explanation of x-rays, their applications in medicine, industry and art, and their danger (and that of atmospheric radiation) to the individual and the species. You learn how radiation therapy is applied against cancer, how x-rays diagnose heart disease and other ailments, how they are used to examine mummies for information on diseases of early societies, and industrial materials for hidden weaknesses. 54 illustrations show x-rays of flowers, bones, stomach, gears with flaws, etc. 1st publication. Index. xix + 186pp. 5⅜ x 8. T622 Paperbound **$1.35**

SPINNING TOPS AND GYROSCOPIC MOTION, John Perry. A classic elementary text of the dynamics of rotation — the behavior and use of rotating bodies such as gyroscopes and tops. In simple, everyday English you are shown how quasi-rigidity is induced in discs of paper, smoke rings, chains, etc., by rapid motions; why a gyrostat falls and why a top rises; precession; how the earth's motion affects climate; and many other phenomena. Appendix on practical use of gyroscopes. 62 figures. 128pp. 5⅜ x 8. T416 Paperbound **$1.00**

SNOW CRYSTALS, W. A. Bentley, M. J. Humphreys. For almost 50 years W. A. Bentley photographed snow flakes in his laboratory in Jericho, Vermont; in 1931 the American Meteorological Society gathered together the best of his work, some 2400 photographs of snow flakes, plus a few ice flowers, windowpane frosts, dew, frozen rain, and other ice formations. Pictures were selected for beauty and scientific value. A very valuable work to anyone in meteorology, cryology; most interesting to layman; extremely useful for artist who wants beautiful, crystalline designs. All copyright free. Unabridged reprint of 1931 edition. 2453 illustrations. 227pp. 8 x 10½. T287 Paperbound **$3.00**

A DOVER SCIENCE SAMPLER, edited by George Barkin. A collection of brief, non-technical passages from 44 Dover Books Explaining Science for the enjoyment of the science-minded browser. Includes work of Bertrand Russell, Poincaré, Laplace, Max Born, Galileo, Newton; material on physics, mathematics, metallurgy, anatomy, astronomy, chemistry, etc. You will be fascinated by Martin Gardner's analysis of the sincere pseudo-scientist, Moritz's account of Newton's absentmindedness, Bernard's examples of human vivisection, etc. Illustrations from the Diderot Pictorial Encyclopedia and De Re Metallica. 64 pages. **FREE**

THE STORY OF ATOMIC THEORY AND ATOMIC ENERGY, J. G. Feinberg. A broader approach to subject of nuclear energy and its cultural implications than any other similar source. Very readable, informal, completely non-technical text. Begins with first atomic theory, 600 B.C. and carries you through the work of Mendelejeff, Röntgen, Madame Curie, to Einstein's equation and the A-bomb. New chapter goes through thermonuclear fission, binding energy, other events up to 1959. Radioactive decay and radiation hazards, future benefits, work of Bohr, moderns, hundreds more topics. "Deserves special mention . . . not only authoritative but thoroughly popular in the best sense of the word," Saturday Review. Formerly, "The Atom Story." Expanded with new chapter. Three appendixes. Index. 34 illustrations. vii + 243pp. 5⅜ x 8. T625 Paperbound **$1.60**

THE STRANGE STORY OF THE QUANTUM, AN ACCOUNT FOR THE GENERAL READER OF THE GROWTH OF IDEAS UNDERLYING OUR PRESENT ATOMIC KNOWLEDGE, B. Hoffmann. Presents lucidly and expertly, with barest amount of mathematics, the problems and theories which led to modern quantum physics. Dr. Hoffmann begins with the closing years of the 19th century, when certain trifling discrepancies were noticed, and with illuminating analogies and examples takes you through the brilliant concepts of Planck, Einstein, Pauli, Broglie, Bohr, Schroedinger, Heisenberg, Dirac, Sommerfeld, Feynman, etc. This edition includes a new, long postscript carrying the story through 1958. "Of the books attempting an account of the history and contents of our modern atomic physics which have come to my attention, this is the best," H. Margenau, Yale University, in "American Journal of Physics." 32 tables and line illustrations. Index. 275pp. 5⅜ x 8. T518 Paperbound **$1.50**

SPACE AND TIME, E. Borel. Written by a versatile mathematician of world renown with his customary lucidity and precision, this introduction to relativity for the layman presents scores of examples, analogies, and illustrations that open up new ways of thinking about space and time. It covers abstract geometry and geographical maps, continuity and topology, the propagation of light, the special theory of relativity, the general theory of relativity, theoretical researches, and much more. Mathematical notes. 2 Indexes. 4 Appendices. 15 figures. xvi + 243pp. 5⅜ x 8. T592 Paperbound **$1.45**

FROM EUCLID TO EDDINGTON: A STUDY OF THE CONCEPTIONS OF THE EXTERNAL WORLD, Sir Edmund Whittaker. A foremost British scientist traces the development of theories of natural philosophy from the western rediscovery of Euclid to Eddington, Einstein, Dirac, etc. The inadequacy of classical physics is contrasted with present day attempts to understand the physical world through relativity, non-Euclidean geometry, space curvature, wave mechanics, etc. 5 major divisions of examination: Space; Time and Movement; the Concepts of Classical Physics; the Concepts of Quantum Mechanics; the Eddington Universe. 212pp. 5⅜ x 8. T491 Paperbound **$1.35**

Nature, Biology

NATURE RECREATION: Group Guidance for the Out-of-doors, William Gould Vinal. Intended for both the uninitiated nature instructor and the education student on the college level, this complete "how-to" program surveys the entire area of nature education for the young. Philosophy of nature recreation; requirements, responsibilities, important information for group leaders; nature games; suggested group projects; conducting meetings and getting discussions started; etc. Scores of immediately applicable teaching aids, plus completely updated sources of information, pamphlets, field guides, recordings, etc. Bibliography. 74 photographs. + 310pp. 5⅜ x 8½.   T1015 Paperbound **$1.75**

HOW TO KNOW THE WILD FLOWERS, Mrs. William Starr Dana. Classic nature book that has introduced thousands to wonders of American wild flowers. Color-season principle of organization is easy to use, even by those with no botanical training, and the genial, refreshing discussions of history, folklore, uses of over 1,000 native and escape flowers, foliage plants are informative as well as fun to read. Over 170 full-page plates, collected from several editions, may be colored in to make permanent records of finds. Revised to conform with 1950 edition of Gray's Manual of Botany. xlii + 438pp. 5⅜ x 8½.   T332 Paperbound **$2.00**

HOW TO KNOW THE FERNS, F. T. Parsons. Ferns, among our most lovely native plants, are all too little known. This classic of nature lore will enable the layman to identify almost any American fern he may come across. After an introduction on the structure and life of ferns, the 57 most important ferns are fully pictured and described (arranged upon a simple identification key). Index of Latin and English names. 61 illustrations and 42 full-page plates. xiv + 215pp. 5⅜ x 8.   T740 Paperbound **$1.35**

MANUAL OF THE TREES OF NORTH AMERICA, Charles Sprague Sargent. Still unsurpassed as most comprehensive, reliable study of North American tree characteristics, precise locations and distribution. By dean of American dendrologists. Every tree native to U.S., Canada, Alaska, 185 genera, 717 species, described in detail—leaves, flowers, fruit, winterbuds, bark, wood, growth habits etc. plus discussion of varieties and local variants, immaturity variations. Over 100 keys, including unusual 11-page analytical key to genera, aid in identification. 783 clear illustrations of flowers, fruit, leaves. An unmatched permanent reference work for all nature lovers. Second enlarged (1926) edition. Synopsis of families. Analytical key to genera. Glossary of technical terms. Index. 783 illustrations, 1 map. Two volumes. Total of 982pp. 5⅜ x 8.   T277 Vol. I Paperbound **$2.25**
                                                   T278 Vol. II Paperbound **$2.25**
                                                           The set **$4.50**

TREES OF THE EASTERN AND CENTRAL UNITED STATES AND CANADA, W. M. Harlow. A revised edition of a standard middle-level guide to native trees and important escapes. More than 140 trees are described in detail, and illustrated with more than 600 drawings and photographs. Supplementary keys will enable the careful reader to identify almost any tree he might encounter. xiii + 288pp. 5⅜ x 8.   T395 Paperbound **$1.35**

GUIDE TO SOUTHERN TREES, Ellwood S. Harrar and J. George Harrar. All the essential information about trees indigenous to the South, in an extremely handy format. Introductory essay on methods of tree classification and study, nomenclature, chief divisions of Southern trees, etc. Approximately 100 keys and synopses allow for swift, accurate identification of trees. Numerous excellent illustrations, non-technical text make this a useful book for teachers of biology or natural science, nature lovers, amateur naturalists. Revised 1962 edition. Index. Bibliography. Glossary of technical terms. 920 illustrations; 201 full-page plates. ix + 709pp. 4⅝ x 6⅜.   T945 Paperbound **$2.35**

FRUIT KEY AND TWIG KEY TO TREES AND SHRUBS, W. M. Harlow. Bound together in one volume for the first time, these handy and accurate keys to fruit and twig identification are the only guides of their sort with photographs (up to 3 times natural size). "Fruit Key": Key to over 120 different deciduous and evergreen fruits. 139 photographs and 11 line drawings. Synoptic summary of fruit types. Bibliography. 2 Indexes (common and scientific names). "Twig Key": Key to over 160 different twigs and buds. 173 photographs. Glossary of technical terms. Bibliography. 2 Indexes (common and scientific names). Two volumes bound as one. Total of xvii + 126pp. 5⅝ x 8⅜.   T511 Paperbound **$1.25**

INSECT LIFE AND INSECT NATURAL HISTORY, S. W. Frost. A work emphasizing habits, social life, and ecological relations of insects, rather than more academic aspects of classification and morphology. Prof. Frost's enthusiasm and knowledge are everywhere evident as he discusses insect associations and specialized habits like leaf-rolling, leaf-mining, and case-making, the gall insects, the boring insects, aquatic insects, etc. He examines all sorts of matters not usually covered in general works, such as: insects as human food, insect music and musicians, insect response to electric and radio waves, use of insects in art and literature. The admirably executed purpose of this book, which covers the middle ground between elementary treatment and scholarly monographs, is to excite the reader to observe for himself. Over 700 illustrations. Extensive bibliography. x + 524pp. 5⅜ x 8.   T517 Paperbound **$2.45**

COMMON SPIDERS OF THE UNITED STATES, J. H. Emerton. Here is a nature hobby you can pursue right in your own cellar! Only non-technical, but thorough, reliable guide to spiders for the layman. Over 200 spiders from all parts of the country, arranged by scientific classification, are identified by shape and color, number of eyes, habitat and range, habits, etc. Full text, 501 line drawings and photographs, and valuable introduction explain webs, poisons, threads, capturing and preserving spiders, etc. Index. New synoptic key by S. W. Frost. xxiv + 225pp. 5⅜ x 8.　　　　　　　　　　　　　　　　　　　　　　　　T223 Paperbound **$1.45**

THE LIFE STORY OF THE FISH: HIS MANNERS AND MORALS, Brian Curtis. A comprehensive, non-technical survey of just about everything worth knowing about fish. Written for the aquarist, the angler, and the layman with an inquisitive mind, the text covers such topics as evolution, external covering and protective coloration, physics and physiology of vision, maintenance of equilibrium, function of the lateral line canal for auditory and temperature senses, nervous system, function of the air bladder, reproductive system and methods—courtship, mating, spawning, care of young—and many more. Also sections on game fish, the problems of conservation and a fascinating chapter on fish curiosities. "Clear, simple language . . . excellent judgment in choice of subjects . . . delightful sense of humor," New York Times. Revised (1949) edition. Index. Bibliography of 72 items. 6 full-page photographic plates. xii + 284pp. 5⅜ x 8.　　　　　　　　　　　　T929 Paperbound **$1.65**

BATS, Glover Morrill Allen. The most comprehensive study of bats as a life-form by the world's foremost authority. A thorough summary of just about everything known about this fascinating and mysterious flying mammal, including its unique location sense, hibernation and cycles, its habitats and distribution, its wing structure and flying habits, and its relationship to man in the long history of folklore and superstition. Written on a middle-level, the book can be profitably studied by a trained zoologist and thoroughly enjoyed by the layman. "An absorbing text with excellent illustrations. Bats should have more friends and fewer thoughtless detractors as a result of the publication of this volume," William Beebe, Books. Extensive bibliography. 57 photographs and illustrations. x + 368pp. 5⅜ x 8½.
　　　　　　　　　　　　　　　　　　　　　　　　　　　　　T984 Paperbound **$2.00**

BIRDS AND THEIR ATTRIBUTES, Glover Morrill Allen. A fine general introduction to birds as living organisms, especially valuable because of emphasis on structure, physiology, habits, behavior. Discusses relationship of bird to man, early attempts at scientific ornithology, feathers and coloration, skeletal structure including bills, legs and feet, wings. Also food habits, evolution and present distribution, feeding and nest-building, still unsolved questions of migrations and location sense, many more similar topics. Final chapter on classification, nomenclature. A good popular-level summary for the biologist; a first-rate introduction for the layman. Reprint of 1925 edition. References and index. 51 illustrations. viii + 338pp. 5⅜ x 8½.　　　　　　　　　　　　　　　　　　　　　　　　　　T957 Paperbound **$1.85**

LIFE HISTORIES OF NORTH AMERICAN BIRDS, Arthur Cleveland Bent. Bent's monumental series of books on North American birds, prepared and published under auspices of Smithsonian Institute, is the definitive coverage of the subject, the most-used single source of information. Now the entire set is to be made available by Dover in inexpensive editions. This encyclopedic collection of detailed, specific observations utilizes reports of hundreds of contemporary observers, writings of such naturalists as Audubon, Burroughs, William Brewster, as well as author's own extensive investigations. Contains literally everything known about life history of each bird considered: nesting, eggs, plumage, distribution and migration, voice, enemies, courtship, etc. These not over-technical works are musts for ornithologists, conservationists, amateur naturalists, anyone seriously interested in American birds.

BIRDS OF PREY. More than 100 subspecies of hawks, falcons, eagles, buzzards, condors and owls, from the common barn owl to the extinct caracara of Guadaloupe Island. 400 photographs. Two volume set. Index for each volume. Bibliographies of 403, 520 items. 197 full-page plates. Total of 907pp. 5⅜ x 8½.　　　　　　　　Vol. I　T931 Paperbound **$2.50**
　　　　　　　　　　　　　　　　　　　　　　　　　Vol. II　T932 Paperbound **$2.50**

WILD FOWL. Ducks, geese, swans, and tree ducks—73 different subspecies. Two volume set. Index for each volume. Bibliographies of 124, 144 items. 106 full-page plates. Total of 685pp. 5⅜ x 8½.　　　　　　　　　　　　　　　　　　Vol. I　T285 Paperbound **$2.50**
　　　　　　　　　　　　　　　　　　　　　　　　　Vol. II　T286 Paperbound **$2.50**

SHORE BIRDS. 81 varieties (sandpipers, woodcocks, plovers, snipes, phalaropes, curlews, oyster catchers, etc.). More than 200 photographs of eggs, nesting sites, adult and young of important species. Two volume set. Index for each volume. Bibliographies of 261, 188 items. 121 full-page plates. Total of 860pp. 5⅜ x 8½.　　　Vol. I　T933 Paperbound **$2.35**
　　　　　　　　　　　　　　　　　　　　　　　　　Vol. II　T934 Paperbound **$2.35**

THE LIFE OF PASTEUR, R. Vallery-Radot. 13th edition of this definitive biography, cited in Encyclopaedia Britannica. Authoritative, scholarly, well-documented with contemporary quotes, observations; gives complete picture of Pasteur's personal life; especially thorough presentation of scientific activities with silkworms, fermentation, hydrophobia, inoculation, etc. Introduction by Sir William Osler. Index. 505pp. 5⅜ x 8.　　　　T632 Paperbound **$2.00**

Puzzles, Mathematical Recreations

SYMBOLIC LOGIC and THE GAME OF LOGIC, Lewis Carroll. "Symbolic Logic" is not concerned with modern symbolic logic, but is instead a collection of over 380 problems posed with charm and imagination, using the syllogism, and a fascinating diagrammatic method of drawing conclusions. In "The Game of Logic" Carroll's whimsical imagination devises a logical game played with 2 diagrams and counters (included) to manipulate hundreds of tricky syllogisms. The final section, "Hit or Miss" is a lagniappe of 101 additional puzzles in the delightful Carroll manner. Until this reprint edition, both of these books were rarities costing up to $15 each. Symbolic Logic: Index. xxxi + 199pp. The Game of Logic: 96pp. 2 vols. bound as one. 5⅜ x 8. **T492 Paperbound $1.50**

PILLOW PROBLEMS and A TANGLED TALE, Lewis Carroll. One of the rarest of all Carroll's works, "Pillow Problems" contains 72 original math puzzles, all typically ingenious. Particularly fascinating are Carroll's answers which remain exactly as he thought them out, reflecting his actual mental process. The problems in "A Tangled Tale" are in story form, originally appearing as a monthly magazine serial. Carroll not only gives the solutions, but uses answers sent in by readers to discuss wrong approaches and misleading paths, and grades them for insight. Both of these books were rarities until this edition, "Pillow Problems" costing up to $25, and "A Tangled Tale" $15. Pillow Problems: Preface and Introduction by Lewis Carroll. xx + 109pp. A Tangled Tale: 6 illustrations. 152pp. Two vols. bound as one. 5⅜ x 8. **T493 Paperbound $1.50**

AMUSEMENTS IN MATHEMATICS, Henry Ernest Dudeney. The foremost British originator of mathematical puzzles is always intriguing, witty, and paradoxical in this classic, one of the largest collections of mathematical amusements. More than 430 puzzles, problems, and paradoxes. Mazes and games, problems on number manipulation, unicursal and other route problems, puzzles on measuring, weighing, packing, age, kinship, chessboards, joiners', crossing river, plane figure dissection, and many others. Solutions. More than 450 illustrations. vii + 258pp. 5⅜ x 8. **T473 Paperbound $1.25**

THE CANTERBURY PUZZLES, Henry Dudeney. Chaucer's pilgrims set one another problems in story form. Also Adventures of the Puzzle Club, the Strange Escape of the King's Jester, the Monks of Riddlewell, the Squire's Christmas Puzzle Party, and others. All puzzles are original, based on dissecting plane figures, arithmetic, algebra, elementary calculus and other branches of mathematics, and purely logical ingenuity. "The limit of ingenuity and intricacy," The Observer. Over 110 puzzles. Full Solutions. 150 illustrations. vii + 225pp. 5⅜ x 8. **T474 Paperbound $1.25**

MATHEMATICAL EXCURSIONS, H. A. Merrill. Even if you hardly remember your high school math, you'll enjoy the 90 stimulating problems contained in this book and you will come to understand a great many mathematical principles with surprisingly little effort. Many useful shortcuts and diversions not generally known are included: division by inspection, Russian peasant multiplication, memory systems for pi, building odd and even magic squares, square roots by geometry, dyadic systems, and many more. Solutions to difficult problems. 50 illustrations. 145pp. 5⅜ x 8. **T350 Paperbound $1.00**

MAGIC SQUARES AND CUBES, W. S. Andrews. Only book-length treatment in English, a thorough non-technical description and analysis. Here are nasik, overlapping, pandiagonal, serrated squares; magic circles, cubes, spheres, rhombuses. Try your hand at 4-dimensional magical figures! Much unusual folklore and tradition included. High school algebra is sufficient. 754 diagrams and illustrations. viii + 419pp. 5⅜ x 8. **T658 Paperbound $1.85**

CALIBAN'S PROBLEM BOOK: MATHEMATICAL, INFERENTIAL AND CRYPTOGRAPHIC PUZZLES, H. Phillips (Caliban), S. T. Shovelton, G. S. Marshall. 105 ingenious problems by the greatest living creator of puzzles based on logic and inference. Rigorous, modern, piquant; reflecting their author's unusual personality, these intermediate and advanced puzzles all involve the ability to reason clearly through complex situations; some call for mathematical knowledge, ranging from algebra to number theory. Solutions. xi + 180pp. 5⅜ x 8. **T736 Paperbound $1.25**

MATHEMATICAL PUZZLES FOR BEGINNERS AND ENTHUSIASTS, G. Mott-Smith. 188 mathematical puzzles based on algebra, dissection of plane figures, permutations, and probability, that will test and improve your powers of inference and interpretation. The Odic Force, The Spider's Cousin, Ellipse Drawing, theory and strategy of card and board games like tit-tat-toe, go moku, salvo, and many others. 100 pages of detailed mathematical explanations. Appendix of primes, square roots, etc. 135 illustrations. 2nd revised edition. 248pp. 5⅜ x 8. **T198 Paperbound $1.00**

MATHEMAGIC, MAGIC PUZZLES, AND GAMES WITH NUMBERS, R. V. Heath. More than 60 new puzzles and stunts based on the properties of numbers. Easy techniques for multiplying large numbers mentally, revealing hidden numbers magically, finding the date of any day in any year, and dozens more. Over 30 pages devoted to magic squares, triangles, cubes, circles, etc. Edited by J. S. Meyer. 76 illustrations. 128pp. 5⅜ x 8. **T110 Paperbound $1.00**

THE BOOK OF MODERN PUZZLES, G. L. Kaufman. A completely new series of puzzles as fascinating as crossword and deduction puzzles but based upon different principles and techniques. Simple 2-minute teasers, word labyrinths, design and pattern puzzles, logic and observation puzzles — over 150 braincrackers. Answers to all problems. 116 illustrations. 192pp. 5⅜ x 8.
T143 Paperbound **$1.00**

NEW WORD PUZZLES, G. L. Kaufman. 100 ENTIRELY NEW puzzles based on words and their combinations that will delight crossword puzzle, Scrabble and Jotto fans. Chess words, based on the moves of the chess king; design-onyms, symmetrical designs made of synonyms; rhymed double-crostics; syllable sentences; addle letter anagrams; alphagrams; linkograms; and many others all brand new. Full solutions. Space to work problems. 196 figures. vi + 122pp. 5⅜ x 8.
T344 Paperbound **$1.00**

MAZES AND LABYRINTHS: A BOOK OF PUZZLES, W. Shepherd. Mazes, formerly associated with mystery and ritual, are still among the most intriguing of intellectual puzzles. This is a novel and different collection of 50 amusements that embody the principle of the maze: mazes in the classical tradition; 3-dimensional, ribbon, and Möbius-strip mazes; hidden messages; spatial arrangements; etc.—almost all built on amusing story situations. 84 illustrations. Essay on maze psychology. Solutions. xv + 122pp. 5⅜ x 8.
T731 Paperbound **$1.00**

MAGIC TRICKS & CARD TRICKS, W. Jonson. Two books bound as one. 52 tricks with cards, 37 tricks with coins, bills, eggs, smoke, ribbons, slates, etc. Details on presentation, misdirection, and routining will help you master such famous tricks as the Changing Card, Card in the Pocket, Four Aces, Coin Through the Hand, Bill in the Egg, Afghan Bands, and over 75 others. If you follow the lucid exposition and key diagrams carefully, you will finish these two books with an astonishing mastery of magic. 106 figures. 224pp. 5⅜ x 8. T909 Paperbound **$1.00**

PANORAMA OF MAGIC, Milbourne Christopher. A profusely illustrated history of stage magic, a unique selection of prints and engravings from the author's private collection of magic memorabilia, the largest of its kind. Apparatus, stage settings and costumes; ingenious ads distributed by the performers and satiric broadsides passed around in the streets ridiculing pompous showmen; programs; decorative souvenirs. The lively text, by one of America's foremost professional magicians, is full of anecdotes about almost legendary wizards: Dede, the Egyptian; Philadelphia, the wonder-worker; Robert-Houdin, "the father of modern magic;" Harry Houdini; scores more. Altogether a pleasure package for anyone interested in magic, stage setting and design, ethnology, psychology, or simply in unusual people. A Dover original. 295 illustrations; 8 in full color. Index. viii + 216pp. 8⅜ x 11¼.
T774 Paperbound **$2.25**

HOUDINI ON MAGIC, Harry Houdini. One of the greatest magicians of modern times explains his most prized secrets. How locks are picked, with illustrated picks and skeleton keys; how a girl is sawed into twins; how to walk through a brick wall — Houdini's explanations of 44 stage tricks with many diagrams. Also included is a fascinating discussion of great magicians of the past and the story of his fight against fraudulent mediums and spiritualists. Edited by W.B. Gibson and M.N. Young. Bibliography. 155 figures, photos. xv + 280pp. 5⅜ x 8.
T384 Paperbound **$1.35**

MATHEMATICS, MAGIC AND MYSTERY, Martin Gardner. Why do card tricks work? How do magicians perform astonishing mathematical feats? How is stage mind-reading possible? This is the first book length study explaining the application of probability, set theory, theory of numbers, topology, etc., to achieve many startling tricks. Non-technical, accurate, detailed! 115 sections discuss tricks with cards, dice, coins, knots, geometrical vanishing illusions, how a Curry square "demonstrates" that the sum of the parts may be greater than the whole, and dozens of others. No sleight of hand necessary! 135 illustrations. xii + 174pp. 5⅜ x 8.
T335 Paperbound **$1.00**

EASY-TO-DO ENTERTAINMENTS AND DIVERSIONS WITH COINS, CARDS, STRING, PAPER AND MATCHES, R. M. Abraham. Over 300 tricks, games and puzzles will provide young readers with absorbing fun. Sections on card games; paper-folding; tricks with coins, matches and pieces of string; games for the agile; toy-making from common household objects; mathematical recreations; and 50 miscellaneous pastimes. Anyone in charge of groups of youngsters, including hard-pressed parents, and in need of suggestions on how to keep children sensibly amused and quietly content will find this book indispensable. Clear, simple text, copious number of delightful line drawings and illustrative diagrams. Originally titled "Winter Nights Entertainments." Introduction by Lord Baden Powell. 329 illustrations. v + 186pp. 5⅜ x 8½.
T921 Paperbound **$1.00**

STRING FIGURES AND HOW TO MAKE THEM, Caroline Furness Jayne. 107 string figures plus variations selected from the best primitive and modern examples developed by Navajo, Apache, pygmies of Africa, Eskimo, in Europe, Australia, China, etc. The most readily understandable, easy-to-follow book in English on perennially popular recreation. Crystal-clear exposition; step-by-step diagrams. Everyone from kindergarten children to adults looking for unusual diversion will be endlessly amused. Index. Bibliography. Introduction by A. C. Haddon. 17 full-page plates. 960 illustrations. xxiii + 401pp. 5⅜ x 8½.
T152 Paperbound **$2.00**

Entertainments, Humor

ODDITIES AND CURIOSITIES OF WORDS AND LITERATURE, C. Bombaugh, edited by M. Gardner. The largest collection of idiosyncratic prose and poetry techniques in English, a legendary work in the curious and amusing bypaths of literary recreations and the play technique in literature—so important in modern works. Contains alphabetic poetry, acrostics, palindromes, scissors verse, centos, emblematic poetry, famous literary puns, hoaxes, notorious slips of the press, hilarious mistranslations, and much more. Revised and enlarged with modern material by Martin Gardner. 368pp. 5⅜ x 8. T759 Paperbound **$1.75**

A NONSENSE ANTHOLOGY, collected by Carolyn Wells. 245 of the best nonsense verses ever written, including nonsense puns, absurd arguments, mock epics and sagas, nonsense ballads, odes, "sick" verses, dog-Latin verses, French nonsense verses, songs. By Edward Lear, Lewis Carroll, Gelett Burgess, W. S. Gilbert, Hilaire Belloc, Peter Newell, Oliver Herford, etc., 83 writers in all plus over four score anonymous nonsense verses. A special section of limericks, plus famous nonsense such as Carroll's "Jabberwocky" and Lear's "The Jumblies" and much excellent verse virtually impossible to locate elsewhere. For 50 years considered the best anthology available. Index of first lines specially prepared for this edition. Introduction by Carolyn Wells. 3 indexes: Title, Author, First lines. xxxiii + 279pp. T499 Paperbound **$1.35**

THE BAD CHILD'S BOOK OF BEASTS, MORE BEASTS FOR WORSE CHILDREN, and A MORAL ALPHABET, H. Belloc. Hardly an anthology of humorous verse has appeared in the last 50 years without at least a couple of these famous nonsense verses. But one must see the entire volumes—with all the delightful original illustrations by Sir Basil Blackwood—to appreciate fully Belloc's charming and witty verses that play so subacidly on the platitudes of life and morals that beset his day—and ours. A great humor classic. Three books in one. Total of 157pp. 5⅜ x 8. T749 Paperbound **$1.00**

THE DEVIL'S DICTIONARY, Ambrose Bierce. Sardonic and irreverent barbs puncturing the pomposities and absurdities of American politics, business, religion, literature, and arts, by the country's greatest satirist in the classic tradition. Epigrammatic as Shaw, piercing as Swift, American as Mark Twain, Will Rogers, and Fred Allen, Bierce will always remain the favorite of a small coterie of enthusiasts, and of writers and speakers whom he supplies with "some of the most gorgeous witticisms of the English language" (H. L. Mencken). Over 1000 entries in alphabetical order. 144pp. 5⅜ x 8. T487 Paperbound **$1.00**

THE PURPLE COW AND OTHER NONSENSE, Gelett Burgess. The best of Burgess's early nonsense, selected from the first edition of the "Burgess Nonsense Book." Contains many of his most unusual and truly awe-inspiring pieces: 36 nonsense quatrains, the Poems of Patagonia, Alphabet of Famous Goops, and the other hilarious (and rare) adult nonsense that placed him in the forefront of American humorists. All pieces are accompanied by the original Burgess illustrations. 123 illustrations. xiii + 113pp. 5⅜ x 8. T772 Paperbound **$1.00**

MY PIOUS FRIENDS AND DRUNKEN COMPANIONS and MORE PIOUS FRIENDS AND DRUNKEN COMPANIONS, Frank Shay. Folksingers, amateur and professional, and everyone who loves singing: here, available for the first time in 30 years, is this valued collection of 132 ballads, blues, vaudeville numbers, drinking songs, sea chanties, comedy songs. Songs of pre-Beatnik Bohemia; songs from all over America, England, France, Australia; the great songs of the Naughty Nineties and early twentieth-century America. Over a third with music. Woodcuts by John Held, Jr. convey perfectly the brash insouciance of an era of rollicking unabashed song. 12 illustrations by John Held, Jr. Two indexes (Titles and First lines and Choruses). Introductions by the author. Two volumes bound as one. Total of xvi + 235pp. 5⅜ x 8½. T946 Paperbound **$1.25**

HOW TO TELL THE BIRDS FROM THE FLOWERS, R. W. Wood. How not to confuse a carrot with a parrot, a grape with an ape, a puffin with nuffin. Delightful drawings, clever puns, absurd little poems point out far-fetched resemblances in nature. The author was a leading physicist. Introduction by Margaret Wood White. 106 illus. 60pp. 5⅜ x 8. T523 Paperbound **75¢**

PECK'S BAD BOY AND HIS PA, George W. Peck. The complete edition, containing both volumes, of one of the most widely read American humor books. The endless ingenious pranks played by bad boy "Hennery" on his pa and the grocery man, the outraged pomposity of Pa, the perpetual ridiculing of middle class institutions, are as entertaining today as they were in 1883. No pale sophistications or subtleties, but rather humor vigorous, raw, earthy, imaginative, and, as folk humor often is, sadistic. This peculiarly fascinating book is also valuable to historians and students of American culture as a portrait of an age. 100 original illustrations by True Williams. Introduction by E. F. Bleiler. 347pp. 5⅜ x 8. T497 Paperbound **$1.35**

THE HUMOROUS VERSE OF LEWIS CARROLL. Almost every poem Carroll ever wrote, the largest collection ever published, including much never published elsewhere: 150 parodies, burlesques, riddles, ballads, acrostics, etc., with 130 original illustrations by Tenniel, Carroll, and others. "Addicts will be grateful . . . there is nothing for the faithful to do but sit down and fall to the banquet," N. Y. Times. Index to first lines. xiv + 446pp. 5⅜ x 8.
T654 Paperbound **$2.00**

DIVERSIONS AND DIGRESSIONS OF LEWIS CARROLL. A major new treasure for Carroll fans! Rare privately published humor, fantasy, puzzles, and games by Carroll at his whimsical best, with a new vein of frank satire. Includes many new mathematical amusements and recreations, among them the fragmentary Part III of "Curiosa Mathematica." Contains "The Rectory Umbrella," "The New Belfry," "The Vision of the Three T's," and much more. New 32-page supplement of rare photographs taken by Carroll. x + 375pp. 5⅜ x 8.
T732 Paperbound **$2.00**

THE COMPLETE NONSENSE OF EDWARD LEAR. This is the only complete edition of this master of gentle madness available at a popular price. A BOOK OF NONSENSE, NONSENSE SONGS, MORE NONSENSE SONGS AND STORIES in their entirety with all the old favorites that have delighted children and adults for years. The Dong With A Luminous Nose, The Jumblies, The Owl and the Pussycat, and hundreds of other bits of wonderful nonsense. 214 limericks, 3 sets of Nonsense Botany, 5 Nonsense Alphabets, 546 drawings by Lear himself, and much more. 320pp. 5⅜ x 8.
T167 Paperbound **$1.00**

THE MELANCHOLY LUTE, The Humorous Verse of Franklin P. Adams ("FPA"). The author's own selection of light verse, drawn from thirty years of FPA's column, "The Conning Tower," syndicated all over the English-speaking world. Witty, perceptive, literate, these ninety-six poems range from parodies of other poets, Millay, Longfellow, Edgar Guest, Kipling, Masefield, etc., and free and hilarious translations of Horace and other Latin poets, to satiric comments on fabled American institutions—the New York Subways, preposterous ads, suburbanites, sensational journalism, etc. They reveal with vigor and clarity the humor, integrity and restraint of a wise and gentle American satirist. Introduction by Robert Hutchinson. vi + 122pp. 5⅜ x 8½.
T108 Paperbound **$1.00**

SINGULAR TRAVELS, CAMPAIGNS, AND ADVENTURES OF BARON MUNCHAUSEN, R. E. Raspe, with 90 illustrations by Gustave Doré. The first edition in over 150 years to reestablish the deeds of the Prince of Liars exactly as Raspe first recorded them in 1785—the genuine Baron Munchausen, one of the most popular personalities in English literature. Included also are the best of the many sequels, written by other hands. Introduction on Raspe by J. Carswell. Bibliography of early editions. xliv + 192pp. 5⅜ x 8.
T698 Paperbound **$1.00**

THE WIT AND HUMOR OF OSCAR WILDE, ed. by Alvin Redman. Wilde at his most brilliant, in 1000 epigrams exposing weaknesses and hypocrisies of "civilized" society. Divided into 49 categories—sin, wealth, women, America, etc.—to aid writers, speakers. Includes excerpts from his trials, books, plays, criticism. Formerly "The Epigrams of Oscar Wilde." Introduction by Vyvyan Holland, Wilde's only living son. Introductory essay by editor. 260pp. 5⅜ x 8.
T602 Paperbound **$1.00**

MAX AND MORITZ, Wilhelm Busch. Busch is one of the great humorists of all time, as well as the father of the modern comic strip. This volume, translated by H. A. Klein and other hands, contains the perennial favorite "Max and Moritz" (translated by C. T. Brooks), Plisch and Plum, Das Rabennest, Eispeter, and seven other whimsical, sardonic, jovial, diabolical cartoon and verse stories. Lively English translations parallel the original German. This work has delighted millions since it first appeared in the 19th century, and is guaranteed to please almost anyone. Edited by H. A. Klein, with an afterword. x + 205pp. 5⅝ x 8½.
T181 Paperbound **$1.15**

HYPOCRITICAL HELENA, Wilhelm Busch. A companion volume to "Max and Moritz," with the title piece (Die Fromme Helena) and 10 other highly amusing cartoon and verse stories, all newly translated by H. A. Klein and M. C. Klein: Adventure on New Year's Eve (Abenteuer in der Neujahrsnacht), Hangover on the Morning after New Year's Eve (Der Katzenjammer am Neujahrsmorgen), etc. English and German in parallel columns. Hours of pleasure, also a fine language aid. x + 205pp. 5⅝ x 8½.
T184 Paperbound **$1.00**

THE BEAR THAT WASN'T, Frank Tashlin. What does it mean? Is it simply delightful wry humor, or a charming story of a bear who wakes up in the midst of a factory, or a satire on Big Business, or an existential cartoon-story of the human condition, or a symbolization of the struggle between conformity and the individual? New York Herald Tribune said of the first edition: ". . . a fable for grownups that will be fun for children. Sit down with the book and get your own bearings." Long an underground favorite with readers of all ages and opinions. v + 51pp. Illustrated. 5⅜ x 8½.
T939 Paperbound **75¢**

RUTHLESS RHYMES FOR HEARTLESS HOMES and MORE RUTHLESS RHYMES FOR HEARTLESS HOMES, Harry Graham ("Col. D. Streamer"). Two volumes of Little Willy and 48 other poetic disasters. A bright, new reprint of oft-quoted, never forgotten, devastating humor by a precursor of today's "sick" joke school. For connoisseurs of wicked, wacky humor and all who delight in the comedy of manners. Original drawings are a perfect complement. 61 illustrations. Index. vi + 69pp. Two vols. bound as one. 5⅜ x 8½.
T930 Paperbound **75¢**

Say It language phrase books

These handy phrase books (128 to 196 pages each) make grammatical drills unnecessary for an elementary knowledge of a spoken foreign language. Covering most matters of travel and everyday life each volume contains:

Over 1000 phrases and sentences in immediately useful forms — foreign language plus English.

Modern usage designed for Americans. Specific phrases like, "Give me small change," and "Please call a taxi."

Simplified phonetic transcription you will be able to read at sight.

The only completely indexed phrase books on the market.

Covers scores of important situations: — Greetings, restaurants, sightseeing, useful expressions, etc.

These books are prepared by native linguists who are professors at Columbia, N.Y.U., Fordham and other great universities. Use them independently or with any other book or record course. They provide a supplementary living element that most other courses lack. Individual volumes in:

Russian 75¢	Italian 75¢	Spanish 75¢	German 75¢
Hebrew 75¢	Danish 75¢	Japanese 75¢	Swedish 75¢
Dutch 75¢	Esperanto 75¢	Modern Greek 75¢	Portuguese 75¢
Norwegian 75¢	Polish 75¢	French 75¢	Yiddish 75¢
Turkish 75¢		English for German-speaking people 75¢	
English for Italian-speaking people 75¢		English for Spanish-speaking people 75¢	

Large clear type. 128-196 pages each. 3½ x 5¼. Sturdy paper binding.

Listen and Learn language records

LISTEN & LEARN is the only language record course designed especially to meet your travel and everyday needs. It is available in separate sets for FRENCH, SPANISH, GERMAN, JAPANESE, RUSSIAN, MODERN GREEK, PORTUGUESE, ITALIAN and HEBREW, and each set contains three 33⅓ rpm long-playing records—1½ hours of recorded speech by eminent native speakers who are professors at Columbia, New York University, Queens College.

Check the following special features found only in LISTEN & LEARN:

- **Dual-language recording. 812 selected phrases and sentences, over 3200 words,** spoken first in English, then in their foreign language equivalents. A suitable pause follows each foreign phrase, allowing you time to repeat the expression. You learn by unconscious assimilation.

- **128 to 206-page manual** contains everything on the records, plus a simple phonetic pronunciation guide.

- **Indexed for convenience. The only set on the market** that is completely indexed. No more puzzling over where to find the phrase you need. Just look in the rear of the manual.

- **Practical.** No time wasted on material you can find in any grammar. LISTEN & LEARN covers central core material with phrase approach. Ideal for the person with limited learning time.

- **Living, modern expressions,** not found in other courses. Hygienic products, modern equipment, shopping—expressions used every day, like "nylon" and "air-conditioned."

- **Limited objective.** Everything you learn, no matter where you stop, is immediately useful. You have to finish other courses, wade through grammar and vocabulary drill, before they help you.

- **High-fidelity recording.** LISTEN & LEARN records equal in clarity and surface-silence any record on the market costing up to $6.

"Excellent . . . the spoken records . . . impress me as being among the very best on the market," **Prof. Mario Pei,** Dept. of Romance Languages, Columbia University. "Inexpensive and well-done . . . it would make an ideal present," CHICAGO SUNDAY TRIBUNE. "More genuinely helpful than anything of its kind which I have previously encountered," **Sidney Clark,** well-known author of "ALL THE BEST" travel books.

UNCONDITIONAL GUARANTEE. Try LISTEN & LEARN, then return it within 10 days for full refund if you are not satisfied.

Each set contains three twelve-inch 33⅓ records, manual, and album.

SPANISH	the set $5.95	GERMAN	the set **$5.95**
FRENCH	the set $5.95	ITALIAN	the set **$5.95**
RUSSIAN	the set $5.95	JAPANESE	the set **$5.95**
PORTUGUESE	the set $5.95	MODERN GREEK	the set **$5.95**
MODERN HEBREW	the set $5.95		

Americana

THE EYES OF DISCOVERY, J. Bakeless. A vivid reconstruction of how unspoiled America appeared to the first white men. Authentic and enlightening accounts of Hudson's landing in New York, Coronado's trek through the Southwest; scores of explorers, settlers, trappers, soldiers. America's pristine flora, fauna, and Indians in every region and state in fresh and unusual new aspects. "A fascinating view of what the land was like before the first highway went through," Time. 68 contemporary illustrations, 39 newly added in this edition. Index. Bibliography. x + 500pp. 5⅜ x 8. T761 Paperbound **$2.00**

AUDUBON AND HIS JOURNALS, J. J. Audubon. A collection of fascinating accounts of Europe and America in the early 1800's through Audubon's own eyes. Includes the Missouri River Journals —an eventful trip through America's untouched heartland, the Labrador Journals, the European Journals, the famous "Episodes", and other rare Audubon material, including the descriptive chapters from the original letterpress edition of the "Ornithological Studies", omitted in all later editions. Indispensable for ornithologists, naturalists, and all lovers of Americana and adventure. 70-page biography by Audubon's granddaughter. 38 illustrations. Index. Total of 1106pp. 5⅜ x 8. T675 Vol I Paperbound **$2.25**
T676 Vol II Paperbound **$2.25**
The set **$4.50**

TRAVELS OF WILLIAM BARTRAM, edited by Mark Van Doren. The first inexpensive illustrated edition of one of the 18th century's most delightful books is an excellent source of first-hand material on American geography, anthropology, and natural history. Many descriptions of early Indian tribes are our only source of information on them prior to the infiltration of the white man. "The mind of a scientist with the soul of a poet," John Livingston Lowes. 13 original illustrations and maps. Edited with an introduction by Mark Van Doren. 448pp. 5⅜ x 8. T13 Paperbound **$2.00**

GARRETS AND PRETENDERS: A HISTORY OF BOHEMIANISM IN AMERICA, A. Parry. The colorful and fantastic history of American Bohemianism from Poe to Kerouac. This is the only complete record of hoboes, cranks, starving poets, and suicides. Here are Pfaff, Whitman, Crane, Bierce, Pound, and many others. New chapters by the author and by H. T. Moore bring this thorough and well-documented history down to the Beatniks. "An excellent account," N. Y. Times. Scores of cartoons, drawings, and caricatures. Bibliography. Index. xxviii + 421pp. 5⅝ x 8⅜. T708 Paperbound **$1.95**

THE EXPLORATION OF THE COLORADO RIVER AND ITS CANYONS, J. W. Powell. The thrilling first-hand account of the expedition that filled in the last white space on the map of the United States. Rapids, famine, hostile Indians, and mutiny are among the perils encountered as the unknown Colorado Valley reveals its secrets. This is the only uncut version of Major Powell's classic of exploration that has been printed in the last 60 years. Includes later reflections and subsequent expedition. 250 illustrations, new map. 400pp. 5⅝ x 8⅜. T94 Paperbound **$2.25**

THE JOURNAL OF HENRY D. THOREAU, Edited by Bradford Torrey and Francis H. Allen. Henry Thoreau is not only one of the most important figures in American literature and social thought; his voluminous journals (from which his books emerged as selections and crystallizations) constitute both the longest, most sensitive record of personal internal development and a most penetrating description of a historical moment in American culture. This present set, which was first issued in fourteen volumes, contains Thoreau's entire journals from 1837 to 1862, with the exception of the lost years which were found only recently. We are reissuing it, complete and unabridged, with a new introduction by Walter Harding, Secretary of the Thoreau Society. Fourteen volumes reissued in two volumes. Foreword by Henry Seidel Canby. Total of 1888pp. 8⅜ x 12¼. T312-3 Two volume set, Clothbound **$20.00**

GAMES AND SONGS OF AMERICAN CHILDREN, collected by William Wells Newell. A remarkable collection of 190 games with songs that accompany many of them; cross references to show similarities, differences among them; variations; musical notation for 38 songs. Textual discussions show relations with folk-drama and other aspects of folk tradition. Grouped into categories for ready comparative study: Love-games, histories, playing at work, human life, bird and beast, mythology, guessing-games, etc. New introduction covers relations of songs and dances to timeless heritage of folklore, biographical sketch of Newell, other pertinent data. A good source of inspiration for those in charge of groups of children and a valuable reference for anthropologists, sociologists, psychiatrists. Introduction by Carl Withers. New indexes of first lines, games. 5⅜ x 8½. xii + 242pp. T354 Paperbound **$1.75**

Art, History of Art, Antiques, Graphic Arts, Handcrafts

ART STUDENTS' ANATOMY, E. J. Farris. Outstanding art anatomy that uses chiefly living objects for its illustrations. 71 photos of undraped men, women, children are accompanied by carefully labeled matching sketches to illustrate the skeletal system, articulations and movements, bony landmarks, the muscular system, skin, fasciae, fat, etc. 9 x-ray photos show movement of joints. Undraped models are shown in such actions as serving in tennis, drawing a bow in archery, playing football, dancing, preparing to spring and to dive. Also discussed and illustrated are proportions, age and sex differences, the anatomy of the smile, etc. 8 plates by the great early 18th century anatomic illustrator Siegfried Albinus are also included. Glossary. 158 figures, 7 in color. x + 159pp. 5⅝ x 8⅜.   T744 Paperbound **$1.50**

AN ATLAS OF ANATOMY FOR ARTISTS, F Schider. A new 3rd edition of this standard text enlarged by 52 new illustrations of hands, anatomical studies by Cloquet, and expressive life studies of the body by Barcsay. 189 clear, detailed plates offer you precise information of impeccable accuracy. 29 plates show all aspects of the skeleton, with closeups of special areas, while 54 full-page plates, mostly in two colors, give human musculature as seen from four different points of view, with cutaways for important portions of the body. 14 full-page plates provide photographs of hand forms, eyelids, female breasts, and indicate the location of muscles upon models. 59 additional plates show how great artists of the past utilized human anatomy. They reproduce sketches and finished work by such artists as Michelangelo, Leonardo da Vinci, Goya, and 15 others. This is a lifetime reference work which will be one of the most important books in any artist's library. "The standard reference tool," AMERICAN LIBRARY ASSOCIATION. "Excellent," AMERICAN ARTIST. Third enlarged edition. 189 plates, 647 illustrations. xxvi + 192pp. 7⅞ x 10⅝.   T241 Clothbound **$6.00**

AN ATLAS OF ANIMAL ANATOMY FOR ARTISTS, W. Ellenberger, H. Baum, H. Dittrich. The largest, richest animal anatomy for artists available in English. 99 detailed anatomical plates of such animals as the horse, dog, cat, lion, deer, seal, kangaroo, flying squirrel, cow, bull, goat, monkey, hare, and bat. Surface features are clearly indicated, while progressive beneath-the-skin pictures show musculature, tendons, and bone structure. Rest and action are exhibited in terms of musculature and skeletal structure and detailed cross-sections are given for heads and important features. The animals chosen are representative of specific families so that a study of these anatomies will provide knowledge of hundreds of related species. "Highly recommended as one of the very few books on the subject worthy of being used as an authoritative guide," DESIGN. "Gives a fundamental knowledge," AMERICAN ARTIST. Second revised, enlarged edition with new plates from Cuvier, Stubbs, etc. 288 illustrations. 153pp. 11⅜ x 9.   T82 Clothbound **$6.00**

THE HUMAN FIGURE IN MOTION, Eadweard Muybridge. The largest selection in print of Muybridge's famous high-speed action photos of the human figure in motion. 4789 photographs illustrate 162 different actions: men, women, children—mostly undraped—are shown walking, running, carrying various objects, sitting, lying down, climbing, throwing, arising, and performing over 150 other actions. Some actions are shown in as many as 150 photographs each. All in all there are more than 500 action strips in this enormous volume, series shots taken at shutter speeds of as high as 1/6000th of a second! These are not posed shots, but true stopped motion. They show bone and muscle in situations that the human eye is not fast enough to capture. Earlier, smaller editions of these prints have brought $40 and more on the out-of-print market. "A must for artists," ART IN FOCUS. "An unparalleled dictionary of action for all artists," AMERICAN ARTIST. 390 full-page plates, with 4789 photographs. Printed on heavy glossy stock. Reinforced binding with headbands. xxi + 390pp. 7⅞ x 10⅝.
T204 Clothbound **$10.00**

ANIMALS IN MOTION, Eadweard Muybridge. This is the largest collection of animal action photos in print. 34 different animals (horses, mules, oxen, goats, camels, pigs, cats, guanacos, lions, gnus, deer, monkeys, eagles—and 21 others) in 132 characteristic actions. The horse alone is shown in more than 40 different actions. All 3919 photographs are taken in series at speeds up to 1/6000th of a second. The secrets of leg motion, spinal patterns, head movements, strains and contortions shown nowhere else are captured. You will see exactly how a lion sets his foot down; how an elephant's knees are like a human's—and how they differ; the position of a kangaroo's legs in mid-leap; how an ostrich's head bobs; details of the flight of birds—and thousands of facets of motion only the fastest cameras can catch. Photographed from domestic animals and animals in the Philadelphia zoo, it contains neither semiposed artificial shots nor distorted telephoto shots taken under adverse conditions. Artists, biologists, decorators, cartoonists, will find this book indispensable for understanding animals in motion. "A really marvelous series of plates," NATURE (London). "The dry plate's most spectacular early use was by Eadweard Muybridge," LIFE. 3919 photographs; 380 full pages of plates. 440pp. Printed on heavy glossy paper. Deluxe binding with headbands. 7⅞ x 10⅝.   T203 Clothbound **$10.00**

CATALOGUE OF DOVER BOOKS

THE AUTOBIOGRAPHY OF AN IDEA, Louis Sullivan. The pioneer architect whom Frank Lloyd Wright called "the master" reveals an acute sensitivity to social forces and values in this passionately honest account. He records the crystallization of his opinions and theories, the growth of his organic theory of architecture that still influences American designers and architects, contemporary ideas, etc. This volume contains the first appearance of 34 full-page plates of his finest architecture. Unabridged reissue of 1924 edition. New introduction by R. M. Line. Index. xiv + 335pp. 5⅜ x 8. **T281 Paperbound $2.00**

THE DRAWINGS OF HEINRICH KLEY. The first uncut republication of both of Kley's devastating sketchbooks, which first appeared in pre-World War I Germany. One of the greatest cartoonists and social satirists of modern times, his exuberant and iconoclastic fantasy and his extraordinary technique place him in the great tradition of Bosch, Breughel, and Goya, while his subject matter has all the immediacy and tension of our century. 200 drawings. viii + 128pp. 7¾ x 10¾. **T24 Paperbound $1.85**

MORE DRAWINGS BY HEINRICH KLEY. All the sketches from Leut' Und Viecher (1912) and Sammel-Album (1923) not included in the previous Dover edition of Drawings. More of the bizarre, mercilessly iconoclastic sketches that shocked and amused on their original publication. Nothing was too sacred, no one too eminent for satirization by this imaginative, individual and accomplished master cartoonist. A total of 158 illustrations. lv + 104pp. 7¾ x 10¾. **T41 Paperbound $1.85**

PINE FURNITURE OF EARLY NEW ENGLAND, R. H. Kettell. A rich understanding of one of America's most original folk arts that collectors of antiques, interior decorators, craftsmen, woodworkers, and everyone interested in American history and art will find fascinating and immensely useful. 413 illustrations of more than 300 chairs, benches, racks, beds, cupboards, mirrors, shelves, tables, and other furniture will show all the simple beauty and character of early New England furniture. 55 detailed drawings carefully analyze outstanding pieces. "With its rich store of illustrations, this book emphasizes the individuality and varied design of early American pine furniture. It should be welcomed," ANTIQUES. 413 illustrations and 55 working drawings. 475. 8 x 10¾. **T145 Clothbound $10.00**

THE HUMAN FIGURE, J. H. Vanderpoel. Every important artistic element of the human figure is pointed out in minutely detailed word descriptions in this classic text and illustrated as well in 430 pencil and charcoal drawings. Thus the text of this book directs your attention to all the characteristic features and subtle differences of the male and female (adults, children, and aged persons), as though a master artist were telling you what to look for at each stage. 2nd edition, revised and enlarged by George Bridgman. Foreword. 430 illustrations. 143pp. 6⅛ x 9¼. **T432 Paperbound $1.50**

LETTERING AND ALPHABETS, J. A. Cavanagh. This unabridged reissue of LETTERING offers a full discussion, analysis, illustration of 89 basic hand lettering styles — styles derived from Caslons, Bodonis, Garamonds, Gothic, Black Letter, Oriental, and many others. Upper and lower cases, numerals and common signs pictured. Hundreds of technical hints on make-up, construction, artistic validity, strokes, pens, brushes, white areas, etc. May be reproduced without permission! 89 complete alphabets; 72 lettered specimens. 121pp. 9¾ x 8. **T53 Paperbound $1.35**

STICKS AND STONES, Lewis Mumford. A survey of the forces that have conditioned American architecture and altered its forms. The author discusses the medieval tradition in early New England villages; the Renaissance influence which developed with the rise of the merchant class; the classical influence of Jefferson's time; the "Mechanicsvilles" of Poe's generation; the Brown Decades; the philosophy of the Imperial facade; and finally the modern machine age. "A truly remarkable book," SAT. REV. OF LITERATURE. 2nd revised edition. 21 illustrations. xvii + 228pp. 5⅜ x 8. **T202 Paperbound $1.75**

THE STANDARD BOOK OF QUILT MAKING AND COLLECTING, Marguerite Ickis. A complete easy-to-follow guide with all the information you need to make beautiful, useful quilts. How to plan, design, cut, sew, appliqué, avoid sewing problems, use rag bag, make borders, tuft, every other aspect. Over 100 traditional quilts shown, including over 40 full-size patterns. At-home hobby for fun, profit. Index. 483 illus. 1 color plate. 287pp. 6¾ x 9½. **T582 Paperbound $2.00**

THE BOOK OF SIGNS, Rudolf Koch. Formerly $20 to $25 on the out-of-print market, now only $1.00 in this unabridged new edition! 493 symbols from ancient manuscripts, medieval cathedrals, coins, catacombs, pottery, etc. Crosses, monograms of Roman emperors, astrological, chemical, botanical, runes, housemarks, and 7 other categories. Invaluable for handicraft workers, illustrators, scholars, etc., this material may be reproduced without permission. 493 illustrations by Fritz Kredel. 104pp. 6½ x 9¼. **T162 Paperbound $1.00**

PRIMITIVE ART, Franz Boas. This authoritative and exhaustive work by a great American anthropologist covers the entire gamut of primitive art. Pottery, leatherwork, metal work, stone work, wood, basketry, are treated in detail. Theories of primitive art, historical depth in art history, technical virtuosity, unconscious levels of patterning, symbolism, styles, literature, music, dance, etc. A must book for the interested layman, the anthropologist, artist, handicrafter (hundreds of unusual motifs), and the historian. Over 900 illustrations (50 ceramic vessels, 12 totem poles, etc.). 376pp. 5⅜ x 8. **T25 Paperbound $2.00**

Fiction

FLATLAND, E. A. Abbott. A science-fiction classic of life in a 2-dimensional world that is also a first-rate introduction to such aspects of modern science as relativity and hyperspace. Political, moral, satirical, and humorous overtones have made FLATLAND fascinating reading for thousands. 7th edition. New introduction by Banesh Hoffmann. 16 illustrations. 128pp. 5⅜ x 8. T1 Paperbound **$1.00**

THE WONDERFUL WIZARD OF OZ, L. F. Baum. Only edition in print with all the original W. W. Denslow illustrations in full color—as much a part of "The Wizard" as Tenniel's drawings are of "Alice in Wonderland." "The Wizard" is still America's best-loved fairy tale, in which, as the author expresses it, "The wonderment and joy are retained and the heartaches and nightmares left out." Now today's young readers can enjoy every word and wonderful picture of the original book. New introduction by Martin Gardner. A Baum bibliography. 23 full-page color plates. viii + 268pp. 5⅜ x 8. T691 Paperbound **$1.50**

THE MARVELOUS LAND OF OZ, L. F. Baum. This is the equally enchanting sequel to the "Wizard," continuing the adventures of the Scarecrow and the Tin Woodman. The hero this time is a little boy named Tip, and all the delightful Oz magic is still present. This is the Oz book with the Animated Saw-Horse, the Woggle-Bug, and Jack Pumpkinhead. All the original John R. Neill illustrations, 10 in full color. 287 pp. 5⅜ x 8. T692 Paperbound **$1.50**

28 SCIENCE FICTION STORIES OF H. G. WELLS. Two full unabridged novels, MEN LIKE GODS and STAR BEGOTTEN, plus 26 short stories by the master science-fiction writer of all time! Stories of space, time, invention, exploration, future adventure—an indispensable part of the library of everyone interested in science and adventure. PARTIAL CONTENTS: Men Like Gods, The Country of the Blind, In the Abyss, The Crystal Egg, The Man Who Could Work Miracles, A Story of the Days to Come, The Valley of Spiders, and 21 more! 928pp. 5⅜ x 8. T265 Clothbound **$4.50**

THREE MARTIAN NOVELS, Edgar Rice Burroughs. Contains: Thuvia, Maid of Mars; The Chessmen of Mars; and The Master Mind of Mars. High adventure set in an imaginative and intricate conception of the Red Planet. Mars is peopled with an intelligent, heroic human race which lives in densely populated cities and with fierce barbarians who inhabit dead sea bottoms. Other exciting creatures abound amidst an inventive framework of Martian history and geography. Complete unabridged reprintings of the first edition. 16 illustrations by J. Allen St. John. vi + 499pp. 5⅜ x 8½. T39 Paperbound **$1.85**

SEVEN SCIENCE FICTION NOVELS, H. G. Wells. Full unabridged texts of 7 science-fiction novels of the master. Ranging from biology, physics, chemistry, astronomy to sociology and other studies, Mr. Wells extrapolates whole worlds of strange and intriguing character. "One will have to go far to match this for entertainment, excitement, and sheer pleasure . . . ," NEW YORK TIMES. Contents: The Time Machine, The Island of Dr. Moreau, First Men in the Moon, The Invisible Man, The War of the Worlds, The Food of the Gods, In the Days of the Comet. 1015pp. 5⅜ x 8. T264 Clothbound **$4.50**

THE LAND THAT TIME FORGOT and THE MOON MAID, Edgar Rice Burroughs. In the opinion of many, Burroughs' best work. The first concerns a strange island where evolution is individual rather than phylogenetic. Speechless anthropoids develop into intelligent human beings within a single generation. The second projects the reader far into the future and describes the first voyage to the Moon (in the year 2025), the conquest of the Earth by the Moon, and years of violence and adventure as the enslaved Earthmen try to regain possession of their planet. "An imaginative tour de force that keeps the reader keyed up and expectant," NEW YORK TIMES. Complete, unabridged text of the original two novels (three parts in each). 5 illustrations by J. Allen St. John. vi + 552pp. 5⅜ x 8½.
T1020 Clothbound **$3.75**
T358 Paperbound **$2.00**

3 ADVENTURE NOVELS by H. Rider Haggard. Complete texts of "She," "King Solomon's Mines," "Allan Quatermain." Qualities of discovery; desire for immortality; search for primitive, for what is unadorned by civilization, have kept these novels of African adventure exciting, alive to readers from R. L. Stevenson to George Orwell. 636pp. 5⅜ x 8.
T584 Paperbound **$2.00**

A PRINCESS OF MARS and A FIGHTING MAN OF MARS: TWO MARTIAN NOVELS BY EDGAR RICE BURROUGHS. "Princess of Mars" is the very first of the great Martian novels written by Burroughs, and it is probably the best of them all; it set the pattern for all of his later fantasy novels and contains a thrilling cast of strange peoples and creatures and the formula of Olympian heroism amidst ever-fluctuating fortunes which Burroughs carries off so successfully. "Fighting Man" returns to the same scenes and cities—many years later. A mad scientist, a degenerate dictator, and an indomitable defender of the right clash—with the fate of the Red Planet at stake! Complete, unabridged reprinting of original editions. Illustrations by F. E. Schoonover and Hugh Hutton. v + 356pp. 5⅜ x 8½.
T1140 Paperbound **$1.75**

Music

A GENERAL HISTORY OF MUSIC, Charles Burney. A detailed coverage of music from the Greeks up to 1789, with full information on all types of music: sacred and secular, vocal and instrumental, operatic and symphonic. Theory, notation, forms, instruments, innovators, composers, performers, typical and important works, and much more in an easy, entertaining style. Burney covered much of Europe and spoke with hundreds of authorities and composers so that this work is more than a compilation of records . . . it is a living work of careful and first-hand scholarship. Its account of thoroughbass (18th century) Italian music is probably still the best introduction on the subject. A recent NEW YORK TIMES review said, "Surprisingly few of Burney's statements have been invalidated by modern research . . . still of great value." Edited and corrected by Frank Mercer. 35 figures. Indices. 1915pp. 5⅜ x 8. 2 volumes. T36 The Set, Clothbound **$12.50**

A DICTIONARY OF HYMNOLOGY, John Julian. This exhaustive and scholarly work has become known as an invaluable source of hundreds of thousands of important and often difficult to obtain facts on the history and use of hymns in the western world. Everyone interested in hymns will be fascinated by the accounts of famous hymns and hymn writers and amazed by the amount of practical information he will find. More than 30,000 entries on individual hymns, giving authorship, date and circumstances of composition, publication, textual variations, translations, denominational and ritual usage, etc. Biographies of more than 9,000 hymn writers, and essays on important topics such as Christmas carols and children's hymns, and much other unusual and valuable information. A 200 page double-columned index of first lines — the largest in print. Total of 1786 pages in two reinforced clothbound volumes. 6¼ x 9¼. The set, T333 Clothbound **$17.50**

MUSIC IN MEDIEVAL BRITAIN, F. Ll. Harrison. The most thorough, up-to-date, and accurate treatment of the subject ever published, beautifully illustrated. Complete account of institutions and choirs; carols, masses, and motets; liturgy and plainsong; and polyphonic music from the Norman Conquest to the Reformation. Discusses the various schools of music and their reciprocal influences; the origin and development of new ritual forms; development and use of instruments; and new evidence on many problems of the period. Reproductions of scores, over 200 excerpts from medieval melodies. Rules of harmony and dissonance; influence of Continental styles; great composers (Dunstable, Cornysh, Fairfax, etc.); and much more. Register and index of more than 400 musicians. Index of titles. General Index. 225-item bibliography. 6 Appendices. xix + 491pp. 5⅝ x 8¾. T705 Clothbound **$10.00**

THE MUSIC OF SPAIN, Gilbert Chase. Only book in English to give concise, comprehensive account of Iberian music; new Chapter covers music since 1941. Victoria, Albéniz, Cabezón, Pedrell, Turina, hundreds of other composers; popular and folk music; the Gypsies; the guitar; dance, theatre, opera, with only extensive discussion in English of the Zarzuela; virtuosi such as Casals; much more. "Distinguished . . . readable," Saturday Review. 400-item bibliography. Index. 27 photos. 383pp. 5⅜ x 8. T549 Paperbound **$2.00**

ON STUDYING SINGING, Sergius Kagen. An intelligent method of voice-training, which leads you around pitfalls that waste your time, money, and effort. Exposes rigid, mechanical systems, baseless theories, deleterious exercises. "Logical, clear, convincing . . . dead right," Virgil Thomson, N.Y. Herald Tribune. "I recommend this volume highly," Maggie Teyte, Saturday Review. 119pp. 5⅜ x 8. T622 Paperbound **$1.35**

Prices subject to change without notice.

Dover publishes books on art, music, philosophy, literature, languages, history, social sciences, psychology, handcrafts, orientalia, puzzles and entertainments, chess, pets and gardens, books explaining science, intermediate and higher mathematics, mathematical physics, engineering, biological sciences, earth sciences, classics of science, etc. Write to:

Dept. catrr.
Dover Publications, Inc.
180 Varick Street, N.Y. 14, N.Y.